THE OPEN UNIVERSITY
A SCIENCE FOUNDATION COURS

G000124165

UNITS 11–12 ATOMIC STRUCTURE

THE OPEN UNIVERSITY

THE SCIENCE FOUNDATION COURSE TEAM

Steve Best (Illustrator)
Geoff Brown (Earth Sciences)
Jim Burge (BBC)
Neil Chalmers (Biology)
Bob Cordell (Biology, General Editor)
Pauline Corfield (Assessment Group and
 Summer School Group)
Debbie Crouch (Designer)
Dee Edwards (Earth Sciences; S101 Evaluation)
Graham Farmelo (Chairman)
John Greenwood (Librarian)
Mike Gunton (BBC)
Charles Harding (Chemistry)
Robin Harding (Biology)
Nigel Harris (Earth Sciences, General Editor)
Linda Hodgkinson (Course Coordinator)
David Jackson (BBC)
David Johnson (Chemistry, General Editor)
Tony Jolly (BBC, Series Producer)
Ken Kirby (BBC)
Perry Morley (Editor)
Peter Morrod (Chemistry)
Pam Owen (Illustrator)
Rissa de la Paz (BBC)
Julia Powell (Editor)
David Roberts (Chemistry)
David Robinson (Biology)
Shelagh Ross (Physics, General Editor)
Dick Sharp (Editor)

Ted Smith (BBC)
Margaret Swithenby (Editor)
Nick Watson (BBC)
Dave Williams (Earth Sciences)
Geoff Yarwood (Earth Sciences)

Consultants:
Keith Hodgkinson (Physics)
Judith Metcalfe (Biology)
Pat Murphy (Biology)
Irene Ridge (Biology)
Jonathan Silvertown (Biology)

External assessor: F. J. Vine FRS

Others whose S101 contribution has been of
considerable value in the preparation of S102:

Stuart Freake (Physics)
Anna Furth (Biology)
Stephen Hurry (Biology)
Jane Nelson (Chemistry)
Mike Pentz (Chairman and General Editor, S101)
Milo Shott (Physics)
Russell Stannard (Physics)
Steve Swithenby (Physics)
Peggy Varley (Biology)
Kiki Warr (Chemistry)
Chris Wilson (Earth Sciences)

The Open University, Walton Hall, Milton Keynes, MK7 6AA.

First published 1988. Reprinted 1989, 1990, 1992.

Designed by the Graphic Design Group of the Open University.

Filmset by Santype International Limited, Salisbury, Wiltshire,
printed by Thomson Litho Ltd, East Kilbride, Scotland.

ISBN 0 335 16330 0

This text forms part of an Open University course. For general availability of
supporting material referred to in this text please write to: Open University
Educational Enterprises Limited, 12 Cofferidge Close, Stony Stratford, Milton
Keynes, MK11 1BY, Great Britain.

Further information on Open University Courses may be obtained from the
Admissions Office, The Open University, P.O. Box 48, Walton Hall, Milton Keynes,
MK7 6AB.

2.3

ATOM

CHEMISTRY

STUDY GUIDE

Besides the text, these two units consist of some experimental work, two TV programmes, an AV sequence and a CALCHEM program.

Units 11–12 cover one topic, the structure of atoms. Two weeks of study time are allocated to these units, and you should aim to complete Section 5 by the end of the first week. During the first week, before Section 5, you should at some time do the experiments, which involve some simple observations using the spectroscope. Try to choose a bright day to observe the Sun's spectrum, although the Sun does not need to be visible. You will also need to view a fluorescent lamp, the long cylindrical kind often used in kitchens, offices and shops.

By the way, in the three Units that follow this one, there is a good deal of experimental work for which you are asked to provide some non-kit items. If you have not already done so, you should obtain these items now: adhesive tape, battery (9 volts), distilled water (2 litres), gas cartridge, household rubber gloves, kettle, matches, sandpaper or emery paper, saucers (3), scissors, small screwdriver, tissues and white sugar. Further details are given in the *Introduction and Guide*.

You will be able to follow the first of the two TV programmes, 'Electrons and atoms', before you study any of this text, but ideally you should first have read to the end of Section 2. You should try to read to the end of Section 5 before viewing the second programme, 'Steel, stars and spectra', although again this is not essential for an understanding of the programme. Notes on these two programmes are in Sections 11 and 12. The AV sequence (Tape 2, Side 2, Band 3; continued on Tape 3, Side 1, Band 1) 'The interpretation of atomic spectra', depends on an understanding of Sections 5 and 6, and so you should use it at any time after Section 6. The diagrams you will need are in Section 6.2.

The computer-assisted learning (CALCHEM) program allows you to practise your understanding of Sections 9 and 10, as well as revising some earlier ideas in the Units. It can be used at the terminal at your Study Centre and at Summer School. It provides an excellent way of revising at the end of the Units and at the end of the Course.

1 INTRODUCTION

In these two Units we make the transition from physics to **chemistry** through the study of atomic structure. For the chemist, a knowledge of atomic structure is the key to the understanding of the properties of substances. Much of our knowledge of atomic structure comes from experiments in which light and other kinds of radiation interact with matter. So, an understanding of light, and particularly of the idea of photons, is crucial to this subject. Much of these Units is concerned with experiments of this kind and with their interpretation in terms of atomic structure. However, before exploring the structure within the atom, we must first examine what is meant by the term '**atom**' and then explore some of the general properties of atoms.

The idea that matter consists of atoms is a very old one, which occurred to the ancient Greeks. The description given by the philosopher Democritus in the fifth century BC of a Universe made up of atoms and the void, the atoms being different in size and shape and incapable of change, is not very different from our modern view although it was based on philosophy rather than science. The idea was revived in the early nineteenth century by the English chemist Dalton, as the most satisfactory explanation of a series of experiments concerning the proportions in which substances combine with each other. In Units 13–14 you will be doing an experiment of the kind that provided the basis of Dalton's theory.

While this type of experiment is best interpreted using the idea that all matter consists of atoms, it gives no direct proof of their existence. Recent

CHEMICAL SYMBOL

ION

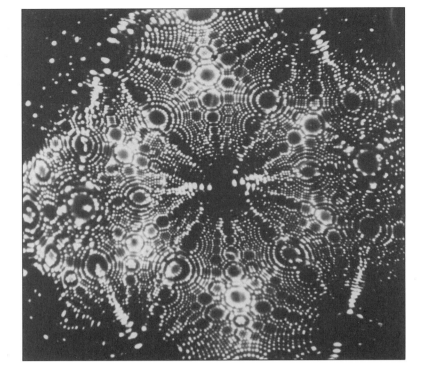

FIGURE 1　A field-ion micrograph of the tip of a tungsten needle. (Photo courtesy of Dr R G Forbes, the University of Aston in Birmingham.)

experiments provide more dramatic and convincing evidence for the existence of atoms. Figure 1 is the photographic image of the tip of a sharp tungsten needle, pictured head-on. Tungsten is the hard metal used to make lamp filaments. At the magnification in Figure 1, about ten million times, the atoms of tungsten show up as spots in the photograph.

We shall return to Figure 1 and how it was obtained in a little while. For the moment we ask you to accept that it shows that tungsten consists of small particles that we call atoms, as do all substances. If all substances are composed of atoms, it seems logical to suppose that different substances are composed of different sorts of atom. Obviously, there are a vast number of different substances. So *are* there a vast number of different sorts of atom?

Your everyday experience tells you that some substances can be converted into others: petrol burns rapidly to produce gases, including water vapour (you can see the water vapour condensing to liquid water on a cold day), and iron rusts slowly when exposed to the air. In the latter example, it seems plausible that one of these substances, iron or rust, contains the other combined in some way with another substance. If protected from the air by a layer of paint or chromium, iron does not rust. This seems to suggest that air is necessary for the formation of rust. In fact iron is the simpler substance, which combines slowly with a component of the air, oxygen, to provide a different, more complex substance, rust. To take another example, you probably know that when you 'burn' vegetables while cooking, black carbon is formed. Carbon too is a simple substance. It also seems plausible that every substance is composed of one or more simple substances, of which there are perhaps a relatively small number.

Although this notion of simple substances first occurred to people well over 2000 years ago, the scientific understanding of these simple substances has developed only over the past three hundred years. The ancient Greeks thought that there were only four simple substances: air, earth, fire and water, which they called the elements. This idea did not stand the test of experiment, and we now know that there are many more than four. Although we still use the term *element* to describe these simple substances, none of the four Greek elements is in our present list. So how many elements are there?

About ninety elements occur naturally on the Earth, and scientists have managed to make about twenty others. Later in these Units you will discover how 'new' elements are made. However, we shall not follow the

TABLE 1   Some elements and their symbols

Element	Symbol
aluminium	Al
argon	Ar
carbon	C
chlorine	Cl
copper	Cu (from cuprum)
gold	Au (from aurum)
helium	He
hydrogen	H
iodine	I
iron	Fe (from ferrum)
lead	Pb (from plumbum)
magnesium	Mg
mercury	Hg (from hydrargyrum)
neon	Ne
nitrogen	N
oxygen	O
silicon	Si
silver	Ag (from argentum)
sodium	Na (from natrium)
sulphur	S
tin	Sn (from stannum)
tungsten	W (from wolfram)
uranium	U
zinc	Zn

history of the recognition and discovery of the elements until Units 13–14. The recognition that all substances are composed of a number of elements took place over centuries of careful experiment and logical interpretation. We start with the view held at the beginning of this century: that all substances are composed of one or more of the 91 naturally occurring elements.

With this number of elementary substances to deal with, the picture is already becoming complicated, especially if we want to describe substances that consist of several elements. To simplify matters, scientists have developed a shorthand notation for representing substances. Each element is represented by a **symbol**, often the first two letters of the name of the element; the first is a capital and the second a lower-case letter. Thus aluminium is Al. Sometimes, particularly for elements that have been known for a long time, the symbol is derived from an old foreign (usually Latin) name. Some of the elements and their symbols are listed in Table 1, and a complete list is given in Appendix 1.

What does the symbol Au stand for?

The symbol Au is our shorthand way of representing the substance gold. But a word of warning: these symbols can also be used to represent the smallest amount of an element. The symbol Au also means one atom of gold.

SAQ 1   What does the symbol Ne represent?

2 ATOMS

Before exploring the structure of atoms, we shall examine in this Section some experiments that tell us of the overall atomic properties, such as size and mass.

Figure 1 was described as the magnified image of the tip of a tungsten needle. This image is not produced by light: it is produced in the following way. In Unit 10 you saw how electrons can be emitted from a metal surface when radiation shines on the metal. If the metal consists of atoms, we might infer from this observation that atoms contain electrons. Under certain conditions, electrons can also be transferred from one atom to another, a property that is used in an instrument called the field-ion microscope. Figure 2 shows how this instrument operates.

The tip of the sharp needle of tungsten is given a high positive charge. The opposite (negative) charge is on a screen in front of the needle. The space between is occupied by helium atoms at very low pressure. In this region between the needle and screen a charged object will experience an electrical force. We say that an electric field exists in this region, analogous to the existence of a magnetic field around a bar magnet (Units 5–6). So strong is the electric field that electrons transfer from the helium atoms to the atoms in the tip of the needle. This forms positively charged helium atoms. Atoms that have an electric charge are called **ions** (pronounced as in lions). As they are positively charged, the helium ions are repelled from the positively

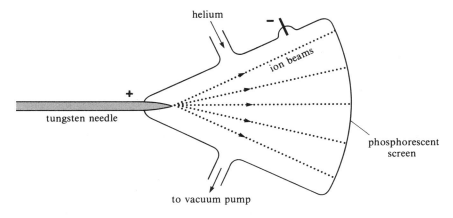

FIGURE 2   A schematic diagram of a field-ion microscope.

charged needle and attracted to the negatively charged screen. Notice that the path they take is along the direction of the field, and the field radiates from the tip of the needle. So the ions travel radially from the tip to the screen. When an ion hits a point on the fluorescent screen, that point glows; this is similar to the way a picture is produced on a television screen. The helium ions are formed at the sites of the atoms in the tip of the needle, so the pattern of glowing spots on the screen is effectively a magnified picture of the tip of the needle. Each spot of light in Figure 1 represents one atom on the surface of the tip of the tungsten needle.

Atoms are obviously very small, so small that the pattern in Figure 1 is a spectacular demonstration of their existence. At the time of writing, pictures of this kind provide the most direct evidence of the existence of atoms, and there are theoretical reasons for supposing that it is not possible to obtain pictures of atoms more directly or with better clarity. Even so, atoms in this Figure appear as rather blurred blobs, not well defined and certainly without any apparent structure. In these two Units we shall be examining less direct experimental evidence about atoms and their structure. The picture that unfolds is one of remarkable detail and elaborate structure, which is completely hidden in the fuzzy representations in Figure 1.

As you might suspect, the investigation of atomic structure requires large and expensive apparatus. But a rough estimate of the size of atoms can be made by a very simple experiment.

2.1 THE SIZE OF ATOMS

You have probably noticed how, on a wet day, oil spreads on a road to produce a thin film, making coloured patterns. Some oily substances spread on water in this way to make a film that is only one particle thick: a monolayer. Each particle of such a substance consists of many atoms linked together, so that the monolayer has a thickness of several atoms at least.* The formation of a monolayer is the basis of an experiment that gives the thickness of the layer, and so provides an upper limit for the size of an atom.

An oily substance that can be used in this experiment is called stearic acid. It is first dissolved in a volatile liquid such as pentane. When a drop of this solution is dropped onto the surface of water, the drop spreads and the pentane quickly evaporates leaving a monolayer of the stearic acid on the surface of water. The area covered by the monolayer can be measured if the surface of the water is first covered with a fine powder, which is pushed apart by the monolayer as Figure 3 shows. The addition of a second drop to this film of stearic acid causes the layer to increase in area. The area is easily estimated by measuring the width of the film in various directions. The results of adding drops successively are shown in Table 2.

> Is the relationship between the area covered and the number of drops consistent with the formation of a monolayer, given that the area can be measured to within a few square centimetres?

Within this accuracy the area of the film is in proportion to the amount of stearic acid in the film, indicating that the film has a constant thickness. This observation is consistent with the formation of a monolayer, and is in fact a necessary condition for a monolayer. However, it does not prove that the film is a monolayer. Nevertheless, the thickness of the layer can be calculated and is certainly an upper limit to the size of an atom since the film cannot be less than one atom thick.

FIGURE 3   The monolayer experiment

TABLE 2   Results of an experiment on the monolayer

Number of drops	Area/cm^2	Area per drop/cm^2
1	32	32
2	59	30
3	106	35
5	168	34
average per drop		33

* The name for a group of atoms bound together is a molecule. The common gases in the air consist of molecules that contain two atoms bound together, whereas the molecules of oil contain more than fifty atoms. We discuss molecules further in Units 13–14.

If the volume of one drop is $0.01\,cm^3$ and if the solution contains 0.05% stearic acid ($0.05\,cm^3$ of stearic acid in $100\,cm^3$ of solution), what is the thickness of the monolayer?

The volume V of stearic acid in one drop is

$$V = \text{volume of drop} \times \frac{0.05}{100}$$

$$= 5 \times 10^{-6}\,cm^3$$

This volume is related to thickness by the expression

$$V = \text{thickness} \times \text{area}$$

The thickness d of the layer is

$$d = \frac{\text{volume of stearic acid}}{\text{area of monolayer}}$$

$$= \frac{5 \times 10^{-6}\,cm^3}{33\,cm^2}$$

$$= 1.5 \times 10^{-7}\,cm\ (\text{or } 1.5 \times 10^{-9}\,m)$$

So we have arrived at a rough, upper estimate for the size of an atom using the simplest possible experiment, based on the assumption that the film of oil consists of a monolayer. More accurate experiments give the diameter of an atom as about $5 \times 10^{-10}\,m$.

SAQ 2 In what way do the spots of light in Figure 1 suggest the existence of atoms?

SAQ 3 Use Figure 1 (magnification $\times 10^7$) to estimate the size of an atom of tungsten, and compare this value with the value obtained from the monolayer experiment. Suggest why the two values differ.

SAQ 4 Approximately how many atoms are there in a cup of tea? (First estimate the volume of a cup of tea, and then assume that all atoms are roughly equal in size and that the atoms are small cubes that touch each other. Use your answer to SAQ 3 as the length of one of these cubes.)

2.2 THE MASS OF AN ATOM

Individual atoms are too small to be seen with an optical microscope, even the most powerful. They are also too small to be weighed, even with the most sensitive balance. However, we can determine the mass of an individual atom very accurately once we have removed an electron from it.

In the photoelectric experiment in Unit 10, you saw how electrons can be removed from the surface of a metal. Because the metal consists of atoms, this experiment suggests that atoms contain electrons. However, an ordinary piece of metal, like any other substance, is not normally electrically charged, so it is reasonable to suppose that the atoms are electrically uncharged (neutral). Yet when irradiated with ultraviolet radiation these neutral atoms appear to emit electrons. As you will discover in several places in these Units, there are various ways of removing electrons from atoms. For example, if atoms are bombarded with a beam of electrons of sufficiently high energy (fast electrons), the atoms may emit some of the electrons that they contain. A fast electron simply knocks an electron out of the atom.

Suppose we bombard the gaseous element neon with a stream of fast electrons so that electrons are knocked out of the neon atoms. The result is the formation of positively charged ions. As with atoms, we can represent ions using symbols to show which atom produces the ion and to show the charge of the ion. A neon atom that has lost one electron is represented by Ne^+. (If one negative charge is taken from the neon atom, this leaves the atom with a net positive charge, hence the symbol Ne^+.) Most atoms, it is

BALANCED EQUATION

MASS SPECTROMETER

found, can lose one or more electrons; thus an atom of neon that has lost two electrons is represented by Ne^{2+}. Notice that the unit of electric charge in this symbolism is the charge of the electron ($-$ for the charge of the electron, $+$ for the opposite charge).

If the symbol e^- is used to denote the electron, what event does the following collection of symbols represent?

$$Ne + e^- = Ne^+ + 2e^- \tag{1}$$

This merely states that when a fast electron (e^-) collides with an atom of neon (Ne), an electron is knocked out of the atom; the result is a positive ion of neon (Ne^+) and two electrons. We describe this statement as an **equation**, and we have used the 'equal to' sign to indicate that the things on the left-hand side produce the things on the right. The numbers of atoms and of electric charges on each side are equal. We say that the equation **balances**. Later, especially in Units 13–14 you will have opportunities to gain practice at balancing equations.

Now that you know how to represent ions, we can describe how to measure their masses. The instrument used is a **mass spectrometer**. Although the mass spectrometer strictly measures or compares the masses of *ions*, we normally consider it to provide values of *atomic* masses. The reason for this is that the mass of an electron is almost insignificant in comparison with the mass of an atom, as we show in the TV programme 'Electrons and atoms'. So, for the remainder of this discussion, we shall talk about the mass of an atom when in fact we are considering ions.

2.2.1 THE MASS SPECTROMETER

The measurement of the mass of an atom by a mass spectrometer depends on the behaviour of an electric charge moving in a magnetic field.

☐ What property do you associate with a moving electric charge (or an ion since this is also charged) that it does not possess when it is stationary?

■ A moving charge generates a magnetic field; for example, the movement of charge in the Earth's interior is thought to be the origin of the Earth's magnetic field (Units 5–6).

In a mass spectrometer, ions are directed with a particular speed between the poles of a large magnet. The field of this large magnet gives rise to a force on the ions, which are deflected from their path. Of course, an equal force acts too on the large magnet but as it usually weighs about one ton, it stays put. If the magnetic field is uniform, the stream of ions follows the circular path shown in Figure 4. Once the ions emerge from the space between the poles, they again travel in a straight line.

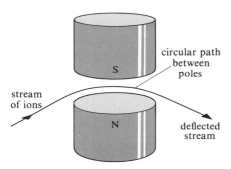

FIGURE 4 The deflection of a beam of ions by a magnetic field.

☐ What factors determine the amount of deflection of the beam of ions travelling in the magnetic field, as shown in Figure 4?

■ The deflection is produced by the interaction of the field of the magnet and the field associated with the moving charge. It turns out that the radius r of the circular path depends on the strength B of the magnetic field and the charge of magnitude q, the mass m and the speed v of the ion:

$$r = \frac{mv}{Bq}$$

However, the speed v depends also on q and m as well as on the potential difference V between the charged plates. The radius of the circular path turns out to be given by

$$r = \sqrt{\frac{2Vm}{B^2q}}$$

Notice that V and B are properties of the mass spectrometer, and so are set in the experiment. The measurement of r (or the deflection) then leads to a value of m/q, the ratio of the mass of the ion to the magnitude of its charge.

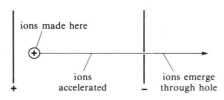

FIGURE 5 The acceleration of ions in a mass spectrometer.

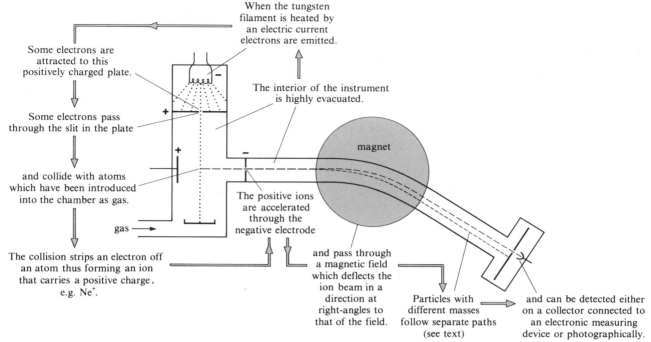

When the tungsten filament is heated by an electric current electrons are emitted.

Some electrons are attracted to this positively charged plate.

The interior of the instrument is highly evacuated.

Some electrons pass through the slit in the plate

magnet

and collide with atoms which have been introduced into the chamber as gas.

gas ⟶

The positive ions are accelerated through the negative electrode

The collision strips an electron off an atom thus forming an ion that carries a positive charge, e.g. Ne⁺.

and pass through a magnetic field which deflects the ion beam in a direction at right-angles to that of the field.

Particles with different masses follow separate paths (see text)

and can be detected either on a collector connected to an electronic measuring device or photographically.

FIGURE 6   A schematic diagram of a mass spectrometer.

To get the ions into the magnetic field, they are accelerated by an electrical voltage to produce a beam. This is done by creating the ions in the space between two oppositely charged plates, as shown in Figure 5. In effect these plates are connected to the two terminals of a battery that provides a potential difference of hundreds of volts.

The ions are produced with positive charges as in Equation 1, and so are accelerated away from the positive plate and towards the negative plate. The negative plate has a hole, which allows some of the ions to pass through, and so a beam of ions is produced. The energy of a particle emerging from the hole in the negative plate depends only on the potential difference between the plates and the charge on the ion. When the ion emerges from the hole, this energy is of course kinetic energy. For an ion with a mass m and speed v, its kinetic energy E_k is

$$E_k = \tfrac{1}{2}mv^2 \tag{2}$$

Ions that have a single charge (atoms that have lost one electron) each have the same energy E_k and so their speed depends on their mass; light ions emerge with a higher speed than more massive ions. So the ion's speed of entry into the magnetic field depends on its mass, and the magnet sorts the ions according to their mass.

Many ingenious devices use this principle to sort ions according to their mass and thus enable us to measure that mass. One such mass spectrometer is shown in Figure 6.

To determine the mass of an atom with this apparatus we need to know only the electric potential difference that causes the acceleration of the ions, the charge of the ions, the strength of the magnetic field that causes the deflection of the ions, and the radius of the curved path of the ions in the magnetic field. Apart from the charge of the ions, all of these quantities can be measured directly in the mass spectrometer. An ion produced by the loss of one electron from an atom (Equation 1) carries a single positive charge. This charge is equal but opposite to the charge of the electron. The measurement of that is described in the TV programme 'Electrons and atoms'.

When these measurements are made, the mass obtained for an atom of neon is 3.3×10^{-26} kg. This mass is obviously *very* small, and not a convenient value to use in calculations. For convenience, scientists often express the masses of different atoms relative to each other. It would seem sensible to choose as a reference the lightest atom, hydrogen, and set its relative mass equal to 1. This was done originally, but it has proved to be more

RELATIVE ATOMIC MASS, A_r

MASS SPECTRUM

RELATIVE ABUNDANCE

ISOTOPE

MASS NUMBER, A

convenient to use as reference a particular atom of carbon with almost exactly twelve times the mass of an atom of hydrogen. To keep the relative mass of a hydrogen atom conveniently near to unity, the relative mass of this particular atom of carbon is set at exactly 12. The **relative atomic mass** (A_r) of an atom X is then defined as twelve times the ratio of the mass of the atom X to the mass of the particular carbon atom chosen as reference. The relative atomic mass of the neon atom detected above turns out to be 19.99.

2.2.2 ISOTOPES

You will have noticed that in the definition of relative atomic mass, we referred to a *particular* atom of carbon, implying that carbon exists as more than one kind of atom. In fact there are several kinds, and their existence is revealed by mass spectrometry.

In addition to providing a means of determining atomic masses very accurately, mass spectrometry provides a method of examining mixtures of atoms of different masses. This is achieved by steadily decreasing the strength of the electric field so that ions of different masses are detected in turn with each ion contributing to an electric signal called the ion current. The result is a plot of ion current against atomic mass; the plot is called a **mass spectrum**. This kind of experiment produced a surprising result when the mass spectrum of the element neon was first obtained. Neon can be separated from the other components of the atmosphere and obtained in very high purity by a process known as distillation. When very pure neon is obtained in this way, it gives the mass spectrum shown in Figure 7.

What do you notice about Figure 7?

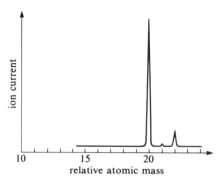

First you are probably surprised to find that for neon there are *three* peaks instead of *one*. Intuitively, you might expect that an element would contain only one kind of atom, but evidently neon consists of three different types of atom, which have different masses. Atoms of an element that differ in their masses are called **isotopes** of the element. Thus, neon has three isotopes. On the other hand, sodium gives a mass spectrum that has only one peak; sodium consists of one isotope of relative atomic mass 23. So, do other elements consist of mixtures of isotopes?

FIGURE 7 The mass spectrum of neon. The relative heights of the peaks give the relative numbers of atoms of each isotope. These relative numbers are called the **relative abundances**.

It turns out that the most of the elements do. For example, Figure 8 shows the mass spectra of magnesium and copper.

Now examine the relative atomic masses of the isotopes that have been mentioned so far in this discussion. What do you notice about them?

The most striking thing is that the relative atomic masses are whole numbers, or at least very close to whole numbers. The probability that this is due to pure chance is so small that it can be discounted. It seems to suggest that atoms consist of common structural units. The relative atomic mass of hydrogen is very close to one, so atoms appear to consist of particles that have masses about equal to the mass of a hydrogen atom.

Can you suggest a way of testing whether all atoms consist of the same particles?

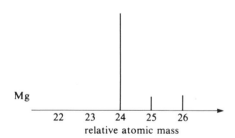

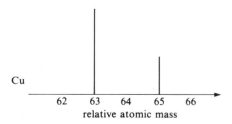

If atoms do consist of similar particles, every isotope should have a relative atomic mass close to a whole number. Perhaps the suggestion could be tested by determining the relative atomic masses of *all* isotopes: if a number of elements have isotopes with relative atomic masses that are awkward fractions, then the suggestion is certainly disproved. So far you have been given the relative atomic masses of isotopes of carbon, neon, sodium, magnesium and copper.

☐ Do the mass spectra of these elements support this suggestion?

■ Yes. The values shown in Figures 7 and 8, as well as the information about carbon and sodium, show that all the isotopes of these elements have relative atomic masses close to whole numbers.

FIGURE 8 The mass spectra of magnesium and copper, shown schematically.

In fact, every known isotope has been found to have a relative atomic mass that is very nearly a whole number. It therefore appears that atoms in general do consist of smaller particles of similar mass to the mass of a hydrogen atom with relative atomic mass of about 1. Later in these Units we shall consider why this should be.

If you want to refer to a particular isotope of an element, you simply specify the relative atomic mass rounded to the nearest whole number. This whole number is called the **mass number**, A, of the isotope. Thus, the three isotopes of neon are represented by the symbols ^{20}Ne, ^{21}Ne and ^{22}Ne.* Carbon, the reference substance for relative atomic masses, is itself a mixture of three isotopes. The most common one is the standard isotope ^{12}C, and this is accompanied by about 1% of ^{13}C and a very small proportion of ^{14}C. This is why we carefully referred to a 'particular atom' of carbon when we defined it as the standard for the scale of relative atomic mass.

Chemically, it is not usually possible to distinguish between the different isotopes of an element. They differ in mass but have the same chemical properties. Consider soot, which is mainly graphite, a form of carbon. ^{12}C soot is black and can catch fire just like ^{13}C or ^{14}C soot!

Since we usually work with substances that consist of a mixture of isotopes, the relative atomic mass of this mixture is therefore important. This is determined by the relative atomic masses of the isotopes present and by their relative amounts. For example, neon contains 90.9% ^{20}Ne, 0.26% ^{21}Ne and 8.8% ^{22}Ne. To calculate the relative atomic mass of the *element* as it occurs naturally (the mixture of isotopes), you simply multiply each isotopic mass by the relative abundance of the isotope and add the products. Thus, the relative atomic mass of neon is:

$$A_r = (19.99 \times 0.909) + (20.99 \times 0.0026) + (21.99 \times 0.088)$$

$$A_r = 20.2$$

A table of accurate relative atomic masses of the elements is given in Appendix 1. If you examine this, you will find that several elements have relative atomic masses that are close to whole numbers. The reason for this is that these elements consist largely of only one isotope. Other elements have relative atomic masses that are not nearly integral, indicating that they consist of a mixture of isotopes.

SUMMARY OF SECTION 2

1   All substances consist of one or more of the ninety or so naturally occurring simple substances called elements.

2   Matter is composed of atoms, which are too small to be seen, but which can be 'photographed' by certain techniques, for example the field-ion microscope.

3   Atoms are represented by symbols, which are also used to represent elements.

4   The size of an atom can be determined roughly by measuring the area of a substance that spreads on water to produce a monolayer. The result gives the diameter of an atom as about 10^{-9} m. This value is actually an overestimate; the diameter of an atom is actually close to 5×10^{-10} m.

5   Atoms apparently contain electrons, as shown by the photoelectric effect. When an atom loses one or more electrons an ion is formed. The masses of atoms can be measured precisely using a mass spectrometer. In one kind of mass spectrometer the ions are accelerated using an electric field, and their deflection in a magnetic field is measured. Atomic masses span a range of about two hundred, but typically the mass of an atom is about 10^{-26} kg.

* These terms are spoken as 'neon twenty', 'neon twenty-one', and 'neon twenty-two'.

α-PARTICLE

6 Rather surprisingly, it is found that most elements do not consist of atoms that all have identical masses. Apparently, an element is not generally characterized by a single value of atomic mass. Atoms of the same element but of different mass are called isotopes. The relative masses of isotopes, using an isotope of carbon as standard, are very close to whole numbers. This suggests that atoms are made up of even smaller particles. We denote isotopes of an element by using the mass number, the whole number closest to the relative atomic mass, for example ^{12}C, ^{20}Ne, ^{22}Ne.

SAQ 5   What does the symbol Hg^+ mean?

SAQ 6   The mass spectrum of mercury is shown in Figure 9. Why are several peaks observed in the spectrum?

SAQ 7   Write symbols for each of the isotopes of mercury which give rise to the peaks in the mass spectrum in Figure 9.

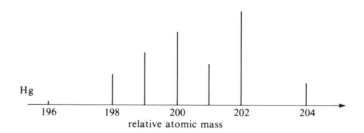

FIGURE 9   The mass spectrum of mercury.

SAQ 8   The relative atomic mass of the element chlorine is 35.45. Suggest a reason why it is not close to a whole number.

3 ATOMIC STRUCTURE— THE NUCLEAR MODEL

Although we have told you quite a lot about atoms, you probably realize that many unanswered questions have been raised by the discussion so far. For example, we have not considered *where* the electrons are in an atom. If an atom contains electrons, it also contains positive charges to keep the atom electrically neutral, so there are positive charges to account for as well. Nor have we considered whether the mass of an atom is spread uniformly throughout its volume. Some of the answers to these questions came from a series of experiments performed around 1910 by the physicist Ernest Rutherford and his co-workers at Manchester University. The picture of the atom that emerged from these experiments is still basically the same as the one we use today. But before we examine Rutherford's experiments and conclusions, a word of warning.

As you have seen in earlier Units, explanations of scientific observations often involve the construction of models. As science progresses through new experiments, old models become refined or rejected in favour of new models to accommodate the new observations. The model of the atom that we shall develop in these Units is not a final one, nor does it account for all the experimental facts that are known. However, it has the attractions of simplicity and usefulness; with it, we can interpret and often predict a wide range of facts. In particular, as you will discover in Units 13–14, the chemical behaviour of elements depends strongly on their atomic structure.

These are sufficient reasons for us to explore atomic structure and to limit the model in the way we have. Where it does have limitations we shall point these out, and towards the end of the Course you will see how these limitations are overcome by the more complex models based on the theory of quantum mechanics.

3.1 THE α-PARTICLE EXPERIMENT AND THE RUTHERFORD ATOMIC MODEL

The best pictures we have of individual atoms, such as the field ion micrograph in Figure 1, show them as fuzzy dots. Their structure is not revealed. To probe the structure of the atom, more subtle experiments are required. Much of the information on atomic structure is inferred from the interaction of light and other particles with atoms.

Some of the heavier elements are unstable. It had been known since 1896 that elements such as uranium and radium emit radiation and particles of various types. We shall have more to say about this phenomenon shortly. Radium, for example, emits **α-particles**, which in earlier experiments Rutherford had identified as helium atoms that were lacking two electrons and were thus positively charged.

☐ What is the symbol for an α-particle that shows that it is a helium ion?

■ The symbol is that for a helium atom with two positive charges, He^{2+}.

Rutherford also determined that they are shot out of the radium atoms with very high speed, more than $10^7 \, m \, s^{-1}$. However, in air they quickly slow down and stop in only a few centimetres. This is hardly surprising when you consider how many atoms the α-particle would collide with when it travels that distance. From the density of air and atomic sizes and masses it is possible to estimate that an α-particle would collide with about 100 000 atoms in a few centimetres. In fact, you might be surprised that it travels so far. This penetration of atoms by α-particles seems to suggest that atoms are certainly not solid lumps of matter like minute billiard balls.

Rutherford saw in the behaviour of these α-particles the opportunity to probe the structure of the atom. He devised an experiment in which a stream of α-particles was shot at a thin film of gold foil, and the scattering of the α-particles in various directions was observed. Figure 10 shows an outline of the apparatus. A small piece of radium embedded in a lead container emitted a stream of α-particles. Remember that air stops α-particles, so the experiment had to be done in a vacuum. The α-particles entered the evacuated chamber and hit a piece of thin gold foil a few micrometres $(10^{-6} \, m)$ thick.

☐ If you assume that the atoms in gold foil touch each other and that the diameter of an atom is about $10^{-10} \, m$, how many layers of atoms are there in the foil?

■ The thickness of foil $(10^{-6} \, m)$ divided by the atomic diameter $(10^{-10} \, m)$ gives about 10 000 layers of atoms in the foil.

When an α-particle struck the fluorescent screen, it produced a flash of light on the screen. By watching for the flashes, Rutherford's colleagues were able to determine the number of α-particles scattered at various angles from the foil.

Knowing that α-particles travel a few centimetres in air before they are stopped, what would you expect the result of this experiment to be?

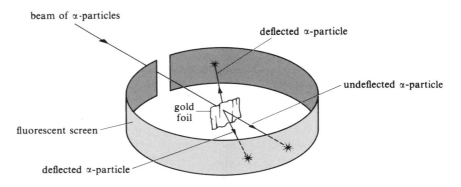

FIGURE 10 The deflection of α-particles with gold foil.

With fewer atoms in their path than in a few centimetres of air, the α-particles might be expected mainly to pass through the gold foil, perhaps with a little spreading of the beam. In fact, most of the α-particles did pass through the foil, largely undeflected.

Does this observation confirm the suggestion drawn from the range of α-particles in air?

Since nearly all of the α-particles appeared to pass through a thickness of about 10 000 atoms *without deflection*, it seems that atoms do consist largely of empty space. So where is the mass of the atom situated, and where in the atom are the electrons and the corresponding positive charges? By patient observations, results were obtained that enabled Rutherford to reveal the internal structure of the atom.

Occasionally, it was found that an α-particle was deflected through a very large angle, back towards the source. So although most of the particles passed almost straight through the foil, some rebounded as if from a head-on collision with something immovable. As Rutherford said in 1936,* 'It was almost as incredible as if you fired a 15-inch shell at a piece of tissue paper and it came back and hit you'. Faced with this curious result, Rutherford quickly established a model of the atom that would explain the scattering experiments. Obviously, the α-particles that are scattered backwards are acted on by a very powerful force.

Can you suggest what type of force this is? Remember that α-particles (He^{2+}) carry a positive charge.

Atoms, as you know, contain electrons, and to preserve neutrality they must also contain positive charges. It seems likely that the force between the atom and the α-particle is an electrostatic force (Unit 9). But electrons are also very light; the mass of an electron is only about 1/7000 the mass of an α-particle. If you have ever played marbles, you will know that a light marble usually bounces off a heavy one without having much effect on the heavy marble, but a heavy marble will knock a light one out of its path. If we follow this analogy, it leads us to conclude that in a collision with an electron, the more massive α-particle is not likely to rebound.

Rutherford assumed, correctly, that the rebound occurred because of the repulsive force between the positive charge of the α-particle and some *positive* charge in the atom. For a sufficiently strong force to be generated, he reckoned that all or most of the positive charge in the atom must be concentrated at a small centre and that the α-particle must approach within about 10^{-14} m of this small centre.

From the analogy with marbles, it also follows that this positively charged centre must carry most of the mass of the atom. (Gold atoms are about 50 times as massive as α-particles.)

It is not difficult to see how Rutherford devised a model to explain this experiment. He proposed that nearly all of the mass and all of the positive electrical charge are concentrated into a small centre in the atom, the **nucleus**. Using this nuclear model of the atom, the interaction of a beam of α-particles and a thin foil (layers of atoms) can be pictured by the paths shown in Figure 11. Most of the α-particles pass through the foil undeflected, but sometimes an α-particle is deflected, occasionally through a large angle. The average deflection is less than 1°, and only about 1 in 20 000 α-particles is deflected through 180°.

Figure 11 depicts the nuclei of atoms as small centres, but even so, it exaggerates the size of the nuclei. Rutherford was able, from the scattering experiments, to estimate the size of a nucleus. The value that he estimated was less than 10^{-14} m in diameter. The rest of the atom (diameter of about

---

* Ernest Rutherford, Lecture at Cambridge, 1936, in 'Background to Modern Science', eds J. Needham and W. Pagel, Cambridge University Press, 1938.

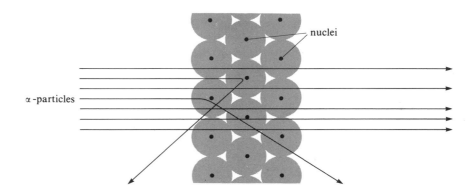

FIGURE 11 The scattering of α-particles by atomic nuclei. (Nuclei not to scale.)

5×10^{-10} m) must contain very little mass and all the negative charge of the atom. Notice that the nucleus is only a tiny part of the volume of the atom. The atom as a whole is 10^4 times as big in diameter as its nucleus!

☐ Imagine that you scale up an atom to fit into a large football stadium, perhaps 300 m in diameter. How big would the nucleus be?

■ A factor of 10^{-4} gives the nucleus a diameter of a few centimetres—no bigger than a golfball.

☐ Can you suggest what the negative charge might be in the vast regions between nuclei?

■ Rutherford supposed that the negative charge must be electrons circulating the positively charged nucleus.

FIGURE 12 Rutherford's planetary model of the hydrogen atom.

The **nuclear or Rutherford model** of an atom with one electron pictures it as in Figure 12, much like a minute model of the Earth orbiting the Sun; in this model the atom is depicted as being nearly all empty space. This model of the atom has the attraction of simplicity, and is adequate to explain the scattering of α-particles. However, it was short-lived; by the early 1920s it became necessary to refine the model, substantially as far as the electron is concerned. As you will discover in Unit 30, the behaviour of electrons is described by the theory of quantum mechanics and they do not obey the same laws as planets orbiting the Sun, which are the basis of the description in Figure 12. In particular, electrons in atoms cannot have such well-defined orbits but must be described in terms of probabilities. So, the electron is likely to be found in a particular region of space in the vicinity of the nucleus. For the hydrogen atom this region is spherical (Figure 13) with a radius similar to that in Figure 12. We call this description of the electron in an atom an **orbital**.

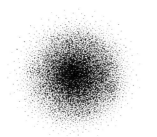

FIGURE 13 A section through an orbital of hydrogen.

This failure to provide a completely accurate model of the electron in the atom does not belittle either the experiment or Rutherford's interpretation of it. There is no doubt that the α-particle scattering experiment provided more information about atomic structure than any other single experiment.

And in fact, the results of α-particle studies were to provide yet more information about the nucleus.

If the force that repels the α-particles is an electrostatic one, what factors affect the angle of deflection (or the magnitude of the force)?

Electrostatic interactions are determined by the two charges (of the α-particle and of the nucleus) and by the distance that separates the two particles. These are related by the Coulomb law, which you met in Unit 9. Application of this law to the experiment should enable us to determine the electric charge of the nucleus, provided we already know the electric charge of the α-particle. The original results of the α-particle experiment were too imprecise to allow Rutherford to determine the nuclear charge accurately, but in 1920 his co-worker, James Chadwick, was able to determine the charge of the nuclei of several different elements by the same method. It turns out that *the charges of the nuclei are exactly integral multiples of the*

CHEMICAL ELEMENT

ATOMIC NUMBER, Z

PROTON

NEUTRON

charge of the electron, *though of opposite* (*positive*) *sign*. Expressed in units of *positive* electronic charge, Chadwick found the following values for the charges of the nuclei of some elements:

Cu   +29
Ag   +47
Ir   +77
Au   +79

In a gold foil, as used in Chadwick's experiments, there are millions of nuclei, each with the same positive charge of 79 units.

Why does not the foil as a whole have an electric charge?

The only explanation is that the positive charge of each nucleus is *exactly* compensated by the negative charge carried by the electrons. Thus, each gold atom is electrically neutral and must have 79 electrons to balance the 79 positive charges of the nucleus. Similarly, an atom of copper has 29 positive charges on its nucleus and 29 electrons circulating in the space surrounding the nucleus. So *atoms* of each **chemical element** are uniquely described by a single number. This number is known as the **atomic number** and is denoted by Z. It is equal to the number of electrons surrounding the nucleus and is also equal to the number of positive charges of the nucleus.

☐ A hydrogen atom has one electron. What charge would you expect to find on the hydrogen nucleus?

◼ For a hydrogen atom to be neutral, the charge of its nucleus must be $+e$ ($+1$ in the units of electronic charge, that is 1.602×10^{-19} C).

A smaller positive charge than $+e$ has never been found. Since the charges of nuclei of other atoms are integral multiples of the charge of the hydrogen nucleus (according to Chadwick's experiments), it can be reasonably assumed that each atomic nucleus contains as many hydrogen nuclei as the number of positive charges on the nucleus. A nucleus of copper would contain 29 hydrogen nuclei, a nucleus of silver would contain 47, and so on. A hydrogen nucleus, H^+, can be regarded as a building block (an elementary particle) in the construction of other nuclei. This elementary particle is given the name **proton** and a symbol ^1_1p, where the subscript denotes the nuclear charge or the atomic number ($Z = 1$), and the superscript denotes the mass number.*

Do all other nuclei consist only of protons? If you refer to Figure 7, the answer should be obvious.

Figure 7 shows that there are three different isotopes of neon, each with the same atomic number ($Z = 10$) but with different mass numbers (20, 21 and 22).

☐ How many protons are there in a nucleus of neon?

◼ There are 10; to balance the 10 negatively charged electrons in a neon atom, the nuclear charge must be $+10$.

What is the contribution of 10 protons to the atomic mass?

These 10 protons can only account for 10 units of mass in a neon nucleus. There must therefore, be other inhabitants of a neon nucleus, and these must contribute to its mass but not to its charge.

Can you suggest what the mass of these other components of the nucleus might be? (Compare the mass numbers of the neon isotopes.)

---

* Often the symbol p (without indices) is used to denote the proton, and similarly other letters are also used without indices to denote other particles, for example α and e.

The isotopes of neon differ by mass numbers of one and two. We can conclude from this that whatever the neutral components of the nucleus are, they have a relative atomic mass of one. It seems likely that this neutral component is another elementary particle, of similar mass to the proton but without charge. This particle is given the name **neutron** and the symbol $_0^1$n. Again the subscript denotes the charge (zero) and the superscript indicates the mass number of the particle.

It is important to appreciate that the existence of the neutron was deduced by the reasoning outlined here, based on comparisons of atomic numbers and mass numbers. Experimental evidence that neutrons actually exist came several years later, in 1932.

All nuclei are composed of protons and (with the exception of a hydrogen nucleus) neutrons. The *atomic number* is the number of protons in the nucleus.

☐ How is the *mass number* related to the numbers of protons and neutrons in a nucleus?

■ The mass number is the *sum* of the numbers of protons and neutrons. Remember that they both have a mass number of 1.

Sometimes it is useful to represent atoms using symbols that show both the mass number and the atomic number, and hence the number of protons and neutrons in the nucleus. For example, an atom of neon contains ten protons, so the three isotopes can be represented by the symbols:

$$_{10}^{20}\text{Ne}, \qquad _{10}^{21}\text{Ne}, \qquad _{10}^{22}\text{Ne}$$

☐ Copper consists of two isotopes with relative atomic masses very close to 63 and 65. Write symbols to represent these two isotopes, showing the atomic numbers and mass numbers. A copper nucleus has a charge of $+29$.

■ The symbols are $_{29}^{63}\text{Cu}$ and $_{29}^{65}\text{Cu}$. The mass number of each isotope is simply the whole number closest to the relative atomic mass of the isotope (that is, the number of protons plus neutrons); and the atomic number is the number of protons (equal to the positive nuclear charge).

☐ How many neutrons are in each of the two isotopes of copper?

■ The number of neutrons is merely the difference between the mass number and the number of protons:

For $_{29}^{63}\text{Cu}$, $63 - 29 = 34$ neutrons.
For $_{29}^{65}\text{Cu}$, $65 - 29 = 36$ neutrons.

A full list of elements and their relative atomic masses arranged in alphabetical order is given in Appendix 1. Inspect this Appendix now, and compare the numbers of neutrons and protons in the elements. For a rough comparison, take the relative atomic masses to the nearest whole number, and ignore the existence of isotopes.

What do you notice about the relative numbers of neutrons and protons?

For all of the elements except hydrogen and helium, the relative atomic mass is two or more times the atomic number, but only a little more for the light elements. This observation can be interpreted by saying that nuclei generally contain more neutrons than protons. This is a useful generalization because it helps to provide rough values of the numbers of protons and neutrons in a nucleus if you know the relative atomic mass. Thus the isotope $_6^{12}\text{C}$ contains six protons and six neutrons in its nucleus, whereas the isotope of gold $_{79}^{197}\text{Au}$ contains 79 protons and 118 neutrons in its nucleus.

RADIOACTIVITY

NUCLEAR REACTION

RADIOACTIVE DECAY

α-DECAY

β-DECAY

β-PARTICLES

Particle	Mass number	Charge/e
proton	1	+1
neutron		
H atom		
α-particle		
electron		

SUMMARY OF SECTION 3

1 The experiment on the scattering of α-particles by metal foil shows that atoms consist of a positively charged nucleus of about 10^{-14} m in diameter, in which most of the mass of the atom is concentrated. The region around the nucleus (diameter about 5×10^{-10} m) contains the electrons.

2 The nucleus consists of protons (of mass number 1 and charge $+e$) and neutrons (of mass number 1 and zero charge). The charge $+e$ is the opposite of the charge $-e$ of the electron. Electrons in atoms were originally pictured as particles in orbit around the nucleus, like planets about the Sun.

3 The atomic number, Z, is the number of protons in the nucleus, which equals the number of electrons in the atom.

4 The mass number, A, is the sum of the numbers of protons and neutrons in the nucleus.

SAQ 9 What do the symbols ${}_1^1$H, ${}_1^2$H and ${}_1^3$H indicate about the particles in these nuclei?

SAQ 10 Which particular observations in the α-particle scattering experiment indicated that the atom contains a small heavy nucleus, with a positive electrical charge?

SAQ 11 Complete the table in the margin without reference to the text if possible. (You may assume that on the relative atomic mass scale, the mass of the electron is zero.) Remember that the α-particle is a helium nucleus.

SAQ 12 Platinum consists of four isotopes with relative atomic masses close to 194, 195, 196 and 198. Chadwick found that for platinum, $Z = 78$. Using this value of Z for platinum, write symbols for these isotopes.

4 RADIOACTIVITY AND NUCLEAR REACTIONS

4.1 RADIOACTIVITY

In the α-particle scattering experiment, the element radium was used as a *source* of α-particles.

☐ If a radium atom emits an α-particle, how do the mass number and atomic number of the atom change?

■ Remember than an α-particle is a helium nucleus, represented by the symbol ${}_2^4$He^{2+}, so that the mass number is reduced by four, and the atomic number is reduced by two. The product has a different atomic number: it is no longer radium!

The emission of an α-particle by a radium atom is one example of a **nuclear reaction**. Nuclear reactions are the subject of this Section. They lead us to examples of the dating of archaeological specimens, reactions in stars and nuclear power plants and the synthesis of new elements.

As we stated at the beginning of these Units, there are about 90 elements that occur naturally. The heaviest of these, uranium (atomic number 92), occurs as two isotopes, neither of which is stable. As you probably know, one of these isotopes is the fuel in some types of nuclear reactor. Atoms of these heavy elements tend to break up spontaneously or **decay** to lighter elements. In doing so they emit radiation, sometimes α-particles and sometimes other types of radiation known as β-particles and γ-rays. We shall now consider the three types of radiation in turn.

4.1.1 α-DECAY

As you know, α-particles are helium nuclei. We can represent an α-particle by the symbol ^4_2He. An example of **α-decay** is the decay of an isotope of uranium shown in Equation 3 where the symbols represent nuclei not atoms. In considering nuclear reactions we can usually ignore the electrons that surround nuclei in atoms.

$$^{238}_{92}\text{U} = {}^{234}_{90}\text{Th} + {}^4_2\text{He} \tag{3}$$

Notice that, as you anticipated, the atomic mass and the atomic number are both reduced and that the product is *not* uranium but an isotope of thorium. Notice too that Equation 3 balances: the mass number (protons + neutrons) on the left (238) is equal to the mass number (234 + 4) on the right; the charge on the nucleus on the left (92) is equal to the total charge on the nuclei on the right (90 + 2). Equations that represent nuclear reactions must balance.

> The sum of the mass numbers of reactants must equal the sum of the mass numbers of products. The total charge of the reactants must equal the total charge of the products.

Later, in Unit 31, we shall consider in more detail the actual masses of reactants and products in nuclear reactions, and examine how these are related to the enormous energy changes that occur in these processes.

4.1.2 β-DECAY

β-Decay is the emission of a **β-particle**. There are two kinds of β-particle, β^+ and β^-. Here we are concerned with the β^--particle, which is an electron. So we shall represent the particle with the symbol $_{-1}^0\text{e}$. The electron, as you know from the TV programme 'Electrons and atoms', has a negative charge, which is equal and opposite to the charge of the proton, and it has a mass of about 1/1800 of that of a proton. Its mass number is therefore zero. In β^--decay, the emitted electron comes from the nucleus. Don't confuse this electron with the electrons that orbit the nucleus (cf. Figures 12 and 13).

□ What effect would you expect the emission of one β^--particle from a nucleus to have on the nucleus? (Estimate the effect on the mass number and charge of the nucleus.)

■ The mass number will remain the same because the electron has nearly zero mass. However, the emission of one negative charge by the nucleus increases its *positive* charge by one. In fact, in the emission of a β^--particle, one neutron *in the nucleus* is transformed into a proton and the emitted β^--particle:

$$^1_0\text{n} = {}^1_1\text{p} + {}_{-1}^0\text{e} \tag{4}$$

Notice that this equation balances, as required.

One of the isotopes of carbon, which occurs in very low abundance, is $^{14}_6\text{C}$ (which we call carbon fourteen). When $^{14}_6\text{C}$ decays, it emits a β^--particle.

□ What is the other product X of $^{14}_6\text{C}$ decay?

$$^{14}_6\text{C} = \text{X} + {}_{-1}^0\text{e}$$

■ Remember that the mass number remains unchanged, but that the atomic number of the nucleus *as a whole* increases by one. The product X therefore has atomic number 7, and from Appendix 1 you can see that it is nitrogen:

$$^{14}_6\text{C} = {}^{14}_7\text{N} + {}_{-1}^0\text{e} \tag{5}$$

4.1.3 γ-DECAY

There is a third type of decay, which involves emission of γ-radiation. This is electromagnetic radiation of very short wavelengths (high energy), shorter even than those of X-rays (Unit 10). Since photons have neither charge nor mass, emission of a photon of γ-radiation does not change the mass number or atomic number of a nucleus. γ-Ray emission often accompanies other radioactive decay processes.

4.2 RADIOACTIVE DECAY

When radioactive carbon, $^{14}_{6}C$, decays as shown in Equation 5, it is converted into the most stable isotope of nitrogen. You might expect that the total amount of $^{14}_{6}C$ on the Earth was therefore continually being reduced. In fact, the total amount stays remarkably constant, because $^{14}_{6}C$ is also continually being *produced* in the upper atmosphere by bombardment of nitrogen by cosmic rays. These are high energy protons that enter the atmosphere from outer space. As a result, the carbon in the atmosphere, mainly present as carbon dioxide, has a constant fraction of $^{14}_{6}C$ in it. When a plant converts the carbon into living tissue, the $^{14}_{6}C$ fraction of the tissue is the same as that of the atmosphere, and it remains the same as long as the tissue is living and exchanging its carbon with the atmosphere. Only when the plant dies or when the carbon no longer exchanges with the atmosphere as in the wood of trees, does the amount of $^{14}_{6}C$ in the plant begin to decrease by decaying to $^{14}_{7}N$, because it is then no longer absorbing carbon dioxide.

Now a particularly important feature of the decay of a radioactive element is the rate at which the decay occurs. Some nuclei decay very fast and others very slowly. Figure 14 shows how a sample of $^{14}_{6}C$ decays from its 'natural' level of about one atom in 10^{12} of all carbon present. This level corresponds to an activity of about 15 β^{-}-emissions per minute per gram of carbon.

> Mark on the curve the time for the percentage of ^{14}C to reduce to half of its original value, and also for the remainder to decay to half of its activity (that is, a quarter of the original value). What do you notice about the two times?

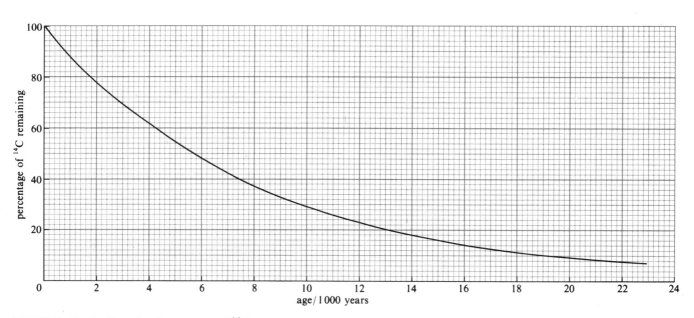

FIGURE 14   Radioactive decay curve of $^{14}_{6}C$.

The two time intervals are equal, about 5 700 years. You could extend this to $\frac{1}{8}$, $\frac{1}{16}$ and so on; in each case the interval would be the same. We can generalize this result: the time taken for half of a radioactive sample to decay is constant. We call this time the **half-life**.

> The half-life is the time taken for half a radioactive sample to decay.

Rather surprisingly, the rate of decay, and hence the half-life of an isotope, is totally independent of the chemical environment of the isotope and of the temperature. It makes no difference whether the $^{14}_{6}C$ exists as the element carbon or is combined with oxygen in the gas carbon dioxide.

An important use of $^{14}_{6}C$ may have occurred to you. Can you think what this might be?

If $^{14}_{6}C$ decays at a known rate (Figure 14) after a plant dies, the present amount of $^{14}_{6}C$ in the dead plant tells us when it died. $^{14}_{6}C$ can be used as a 'clock' for a time-scale covering tens of thousands of years. This is the time-scale of civilization, so $^{14}_{6}C$ provides a means of dating archaeological specimens by a method called **carbon dating**.

To calculate the age of an artefact by carbon dating it is useful to have an expression that relates the amount of $^{14}_{6}C$ in the sample and the amount of $^{14}_{6}C$ that was originally present. Such an expression can be established from the information in Table 3.

TABLE 3   Radioactive decay of $^{14}_{6}C$

Number of half lives n	Remaining activity	
	As fraction	As exponential
0	1	$(\frac{1}{2})^0$
1	$\frac{1}{2}$	
2	$\frac{1}{4}$	
3	$\frac{1}{8}$	
4	$\frac{1}{16}$	

We can express all of the fractions in Table 3 in an exponential form, that is as $\frac{1}{2}$ raised to the power of some exponent. The value $\frac{1}{2}$ is of course expressed as $(\frac{1}{2})^1$. The value 1, at the start of the decay, is equal to $(\frac{1}{2})^0$. Although you may not be familiar with this equality, in fact any number x to the power zero is equal to one: $x^0 = 1$ (*MAFS*, Block 1). So you can now complete the last column of Table 3, by entering $(\frac{1}{2})^1$, $(\frac{1}{2})^2$, etc.

□ If we have a sample that originally contains N_0 atoms of $^{14}_{6}C$, how many atoms of $^{14}_{6}C$ does it contain after four half-lives?

■ The fraction of $^{14}_{6}C$ remaining is $(\frac{1}{2})^4$, from extrapolation of the data in Table 3. So the number of $^{14}_{6}C$ atoms is $N_0 \times (\frac{1}{2})^4$.

This leads us immediately to an expression for the **exponential decay** of $^{14}_{6}C$.

□ Write an expression for the number N of $^{14}_{6}C$ nuclei left after n half-lives, starting with N_0 nuclei.

■ The fraction remaining after n half-lives is $(\frac{1}{2})^n$, so the number is $N_0 \times (\frac{1}{2})^n$.

Therefore we may write the general expression for the number N of radioactive nuclei left after n half-lives as

$$N = N_0 \times (\tfrac{1}{2})^n \tag{6}$$

This kind of expression, involving a term (in this case $\frac{1}{2}$) with an exponent (n), is called an exponential expression. We say that the rate of a radioactive decay is exponential. You will come across more examples of exponential decay and growth in later Units of the Course.

An important application of carbon dating was in the estimation of the age of the Dead Sea Scrolls, which were discovered in a cave on the north-west shore of the Dead Sea. It was found that the level of radioactivity in a sample of the linen in which the scrolls were wrapped was about 78% of the original activity, based on the known original abundance of $^{14}_{6}C$ in the linen.

☐ Use this value and Figure 14 to estimate the age of the scrolls.

■ From Figure 14, a level of radioactivity corresponding to 78% of the $^{14}_{6}C$ nuclei remaining indicates an age of a little over 2 000 years for the linen.

This proves that the scrolls are about 2 000 years old, although they are not necessarily a contemporary record of the Book of Isaiah (about 500 BC).

$^{14}_{6}C$ is just one of the many radioactive isotopes. Others, for example some of those in Table 4, have very long half-lives, on the time-scale of geological processes. Dating of geological specimens will be discussed in Units 28–29.

4.3 NUCLEAR FISSION AND NUCLEAR FUSION

The product of radioactive decay is normally an isotope with an atomic number close to that of the original isotope. However, in 1939 two German scientists, Otto Hahn and Fritz Strassmann, discovered that the element barium is a product of the radioactive isotope $^{235}_{92}U$. Barium has an atomic number of 56, and in the decomposition of $^{235}_{92}U$ neutrons are also produced. In fact, they take part in the reaction.

☐ What is the other product of the following reaction?

$$^{235}_{92}U + ^{1}_{0}n = ^{144}_{56}Ba + 3^{1}_{0}n + ? \tag{7}$$

■ Because the total mass number and charge are conserved in nuclear reactions, the atomic number of the product is

$$92 - 56 = 36$$

and the mass number is

$$(235 + 1) - (144 + 3) = 89$$

As you can tell from Appendix 1, element number 36 is krypton, so the product is $^{89}_{36}Kr$.

You can see that Equation 7 represents a process quite different from a simple radioactive decay. When bombarded by neutrons, the $^{235}_{92}U$ nucleus splits into two smaller nuclei plus more neutrons. This splitting process is known as **nuclear fission**. The reaction shown in Equation 7 occurs in the fuel elements of some nuclear power stations and in the early types of nuclear bomb. As you know, vast quantities of energy are released in nuclear fission. You will probably have noticed too that the date of Hahn and Strassmann's discovery was just before the outbreak of the Second World War. The flurry of research into nuclear fission which followed resulted in the USA being first to develop a nuclear power station and the 'Atomic Bomb'.

Now, more than forty years later, we think of the hydrogen bomb as the current atomic weapon. Just as heavy nuclei break down to lighter ones, so very light nuclei can be made to *fuse* to form heavier ones. In the hydrogen bomb we are in fact simulating, on a relatively minute scale, the nuclear processes that occur in the Sun. For example, deuterium atoms, which are isotopes of hydrogen consisting of one proton and one neutron, combine to form helium atoms in a process called **nuclear fusion**:

$$^{2}_{1}H + ^{2}_{1}H = ^{4}_{2}He \tag{8}$$

TABLE 4 The half-lives of some isotopes

Isotope	Half-life
$^{3}_{1}H$	12.26 years
$^{6}_{4}Be$	4×10^{-21} seconds
$^{7}_{4}Be$	53 days
$^{8}_{4}Be$	2×10^{-16} seconds
$^{9}_{4}Be$	stable*
$^{10}_{4}Be$	2.5×10^{6} years
$^{11}_{4}Be$	13.6 seconds
$^{10}_{6}C$	19 seconds
$^{11}_{6}C$	20.3 minutes
$^{12}_{6}C$	stable*
$^{13}_{6}C$	stable*
$^{14}_{6}C$	5 730 years*
$^{15}_{6}C$	2.4 seconds
$^{16}_{6}C$	0.74 seconds
$^{18}_{9}F$	1.83 hours
$^{19}_{9}F$	stable*
$^{22}_{11}Na$	2.60 years
$^{23}_{11}Na$	stable*
$^{32}_{15}P$	14.3 days
$^{32}_{16}S$	stable*
$^{35}_{16}S$	88 days
$^{40}_{19}K$	1.28×10^{9} years*
$^{40}_{20}Ca$	stable*
$^{87}_{37}Rb$	5.0×10^{11} years*
$^{90}_{38}Sr$	28 years
$^{137}_{55}Cs$	30 years
$^{235}_{92}U$	7.1×10^{8} years*
$^{238}_{92}U$	4.51×10^{9} years*

* Occurs naturally

We examine the composition of the Sun and other stars in the TV programme 'Steel, stars and spectra'. In Unit 31 we shall return to the topic of energy release in nuclear reactions. For the moment you should know as much about the nucleus of an atom as you need to understand the model of the atom that we shall develop in these Units.

SUMMARY OF SECTION 4

1   There are about 90 elements with stable isotopes; elements heavier than those with atomic number 90 are generally unstable.

2   Unstable isotopes decompose by emitting α- or β-particles and γ-radiation, or by nuclear fission.

3   The time taken for half of a sample of radioactive nuclei to decay is characteristic of that nucleus and is called a half-life.

4   The rate of radioactive decay is exponential.

5   The decay of $^{14}_{6}C$ provides a means of dating archaeological specimens.

SAQ 13   A sample of cedar wood taken from the Egyptian pyramid at Snefuru has an activity corresponding to 55% of the present natural abundance of $^{14}_{6}C$. How old is the sample?

SAQ 14   In 1932 in a series of experiments with α-particles, Chadwick bombarded atoms of boron (symbol B) with α-particles and produced carbon-12. What was the other product?

$$^{9}_{4}B + ^{4}_{2}He = ^{12}_{6}C + ?$$

SAQ 15   In a nuclear reactor, $^{235}_{92}U$ undergoes fission and releases free neutrons. If another isotope of uranium $^{238}_{92}U$ is present, it captures a neutron, but subsequently emits two β^{-}-particles (electrons, $^{0}_{-1}e$). What is the atomic number of the product?

$$^{238}_{92}U + ^{1}_{0}n = ? + 2\,^{0}_{-1}e$$

SAQ 16   Nuclear reactions have been exploited in making several new heavy elements. What is the atomic number of the element produced in the following processes, in which $^{238}_{92}U$ is bombarded with carbon nuclei, $^{12}_{6}C$?

$$^{238}_{92}U + ^{12}_{6}C = ? + 4\,^{1}_{0}n$$

5 ATOMIC SPECTRA

With the broad picture of the atom that we developed in Section 3, we shall now proceed to examine in a little more detail the arrangement of electrons in atoms. If you are wondering where this exploration of atomic structure is leading, please be patient. In Units 13–14 you will encounter one of the most important scientific relationships to be discovered in the past century: the relationship between chemical behaviour and atomic structure.

Consider the three elements fluorine, neon and sodium. Their atomic numbers are 9, 10 and 11, respectively. These numbers are also equal to the charges of the nuclei of these elements and to the numbers of electrons that their atoms contain. So what effects do these numbers have on their chemical properties?

Fluorine is a gas that reacts with almost all substances, usually vigorously. Neon is also a gas, but has not been found to react with any substance. Sodium is a metal, and reacts violently with water and air. In Units 13–14 you will discover that the arrangement of electrons in the atoms of these three very dissimilar elements provides an explanation for these properties. Consequently, for the remainder of these two Units, we shall explore the **electronic structure** of atoms.

Just as we cannot 'see' atoms directly, neither can we 'see' the arrangements of electrons in atoms. However, radiation of various sorts interacts with the electrons in atoms, revealing information that allows us to construct a model of the electronic structure of atoms. To begin, we shall investigate how electromagnetic radiation, and particularly light, interacts with electrons in atoms.

Please do Experiment 1 now, before answering ITQ 1 below.

ITQ 1   Are you now able to suggest what source is used in the bluish-white street lights?

In all the spectra you have seen, except the white-light spectrum, you will have observed distinct bright lines. These bright lines result from atoms that acquired energy from an electric discharge in the lamps. The energy is subsequently emitted by the atoms as radiation of particular frequencies. Since these spectra arise from atoms, we call them **atomic spectra**, and because they consist of lines they are also called **line spectra**.

If you have had the opportunity to observe several different sources, you will have noticed that each source gives rise to its own characteristic coloured line, or set of lines. The pattern is characteristic of the element producing the spectrum.

What use does this suggest for atomic spectroscopy?

EXPERIMENT 1

TIME

This experiment takes about 20 minutes

KIT ITEM

Part 1

Spectroscope

SPECTRA

This experiment and the next consist of some simple observations with the spectroscope in the Experiment Kit. This is the only piece of apparatus you need. These observations show you various kinds of spectrum and illustrate how electronic structure is derived from experimental observation.

PART 1   THE WHITE-LIGHT SPECTRUM

Examine the spectroscope. One end slides in and out. This is the end that you look through. The other end has a slit in it. Look through the spectroscope at an ordinary light-bulb. When you point the end with the fine slit in it towards the bulb, you should see a spectrum of colours resembling Spectrum A on the colour plate. Hold the spectroscope so that the colours range from red on your left to violet on your right, and slide the lens-holder part of the spectroscope in and out until the spectrum has sharp upper and lower edges. It is now roughly in focus. The spectrum ranges continuously from red to violet (and beyond, although you cannot see outside this range). It is produced by the *emission* of radiation by the hot wire in the lamp, and is called an **emission spectrum**. Light that gives a **continuous spectrum** like that in Spectrum A of the colour plate, containing all possible frequencies of visible radiation, is known as white light.

PART 2   THE MERCURY VAPOUR SPECTRUM

Now examine the spectrum of a fluorescent lamp (a mercury lamp) of the kind often used in kitchens, offices and shops. For best results get close to the lamp; about a foot away will do. At the first attempt you may see a number of broad coloured bands. You may need to slide the focusing lens in or out to sharpen the picture until the bands become lines. You will probably find that you cannot bring all the lines into focus at the same time. (The best position of the focusing lens for, say, a yellow line is different from that for a violet line.)

Sketch in your Notebook what you see, on the same scale as the white-light spectrum in the colour plate (Spectrum A). This should be easy, because, as background to the mercury spectrum, you will also see a continuous white-light spectrum from a fluorescent substance, which coats the inside of the lamp.

If you have access to sodium street lights (these are the yellow ones), to bluish-white street lights, or to any of the various red and blue lights collectively (but wrongly) described as 'neon lights', view these with the spectroscope and draw in your Notebook diagrams of what you see. The colour plate shows the spectra of some of these lights. Compare your sketches with the spectra in the colour plate.

Atomic spectra, being characteristic of the elements that produce them, provide a means of analytical identification of elements. You will meet atomic spectroscopy again in Units 13–14 and we illustrate its use in the TV programme 'Steel, stars and spectra'.

EXPERIMENT 2   THE SOLAR SPECTRUM

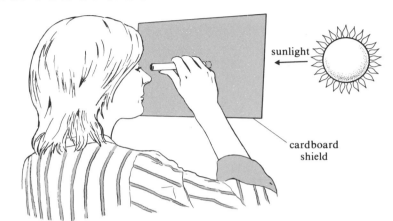

FIGURE 15   Using the spectroscope to observe the Sun's spectrum.

Sunlight enables us to see objects of all colours. You might, therefore, reasonably conclude that sunlight is genuinely white light, as in Spectrum A. Take a piece of card and make a hole in it that will take the spectroscope. Then point your spectroscope close to but not directly at the Sun, as shown in Figure 15. The card will shield your eyes from direct sunlight. Now focus your spectroscope on any lines that you can observe. The dark lines you should be able to see are called **Fraunhofer lines** after their discovery by Joseph Fraunhofer in 1814. You can observe the Sun's spectrum on a cloudy day, although the lines are not so evident. Sketch the position of these lines on the same scale as the white-light spectrum in Spectrum A.

If the bright lines you observed in the mercury spectrum are *emission* lines, what would you call the dark lines in the Sun's spectrum?

Dark lines must result from the removal or *absorption* of light of certain frequencies from the white light emitted by the hot part of the Sun, producing an **absorption spectrum**. Atoms in the Sun's atmosphere absorb particular frequencies, leaving gaps in the continuous spectrum (Figure 16). It may not surprise you to learn that the frequencies absorbed by an atom are identical with those that the same atom emits when heated. We have already indicated that these frequencies are characteristic of the particular atom involved. (This point is illustrated in the TV programme 'Steel, stars and spectra', and its significance will be discussed in more detail in a later Section.)

Now compare your Fraunhofer absorption spectrum with the various atomic emission spectra illustrated on the colour plate, and suggest whether any of these atoms may be present in significant amounts in the Sun.

ITQ 2   What elements can you detect in the Sun's spectrum?

Obviously, atomic spectroscopy has fascinating and far-reaching applications. It is remarkable that, with such a simple piece of equipment, we can begin to analyse the Sun at a distance of about 1.5×10^{11} m!). But for our present purposes, we are more concerned with probing the structure of the atom (about 5×10^{-10} m in diameter) with the same technique.

SOLAR SPECTRUM

FRAUNHOFER LINES

ABSORPTION SPECTRUM

QUANTIZATION OF ENERGY

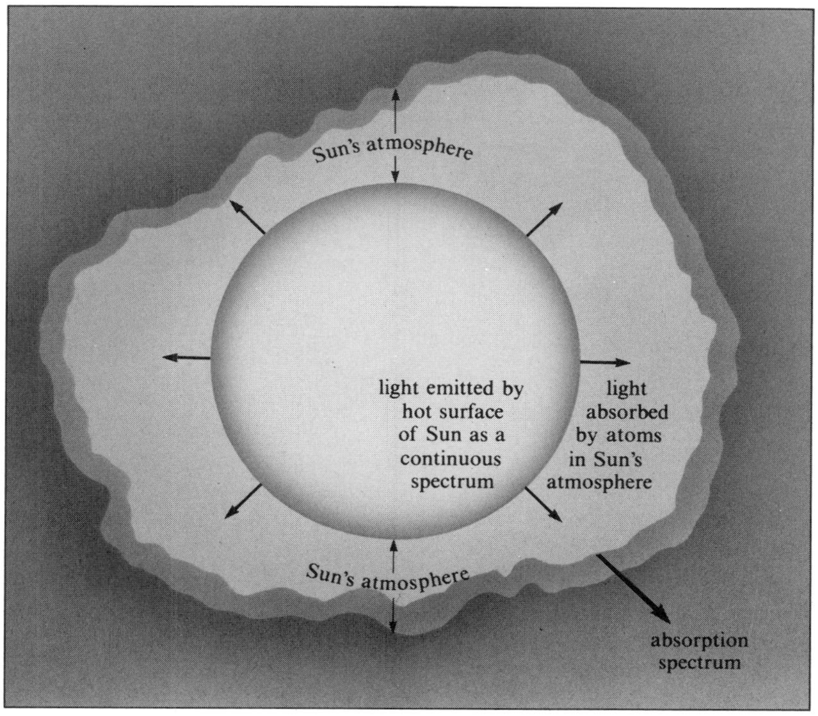

FIGURE 16 How Fraunhofer lines are produced.

5.1 THE SIGNIFICANCE OF LINE SPECTRA

The line spectra you have examined with your spectroscope are not only beautiful, they are highly significant. They are direct evidence for a phenomenon that is quite outside our normal experience. Everything in our experience conditions us to think of energy as being continuously variable. As we cycle downhill, the bicycle moves smoothly faster and faster as it smoothly acquires kinetic energy; a billiard ball, once struck by a cue, slowly loses its kinetic energy until eventually it stops; a firework rocket shot in the air smoothly acquires gravitational energy as it goes up and smoothly loses it as it comes down. There are no restrictions on the energy changes possible in any of these systems. It was the cause of some consternation, therefore, when it was suggested at the end of the last century that atoms are restricted in the way they can change their energy.

As we shall demonstrate, the discrete frequencies of line spectra show that an atom can change its energy only by certain fixed amounts. The energy possibilities for an atom are *not* continuously variable as they are, for example, for the ball on a billiard table. You know that when a stationary billiard ball is hit by another ball, the two exchange energy whatever the energy of the moving ball. If the stationary ball were to behave like an atom, it would be choosy about the magnitude of the energy which it would exchange. It could adopt only 'permitted' energies, and would be unable to interact with bodies that did not supply this exact energy.

Section 6.2 of Unit 10 makes the point that when light interacts with matter, it is best described not as a continuous wave but as a stream of little packets of energy called photons: the energy of light is said to be **quantized**. The discrete frequencies of atomic spectra show that the atom's energy is also *quantized*. Let us look at a simple spectrum in more detail to interpret the significance of these quantized energy changes.

5.1.1 THE SPECTRUM OF ATOMIC HYDROGEN

If we wish to interpret line spectra, it makes sense to start with the simplest case. The hydrogen atom, as you will recall from Section 3, contains only one proton in the nucleus and one electron outside it. The energy of a system like this depends on how the electron and proton are arranged with

ELECTRON ENERGY LEVEL

ELECTRON ENERGY-LEVEL
DIAGRAM

respect to each other. It follows that the only energy changes the hydrogen atom can undergo are those that result from changes in the relative positions of the electron and the proton.

☐ What does the electrostatic force between oppositely charged particles depend on? (You should remember this from Unit 9.)

■ The electrostatic attraction between oppositely charged bodies is described by Coulomb's law (Unit 9, Section 9.2). The force depends on the distance between the charged bodies; it decreases with increasing distance. (It also depends on the magnitudes of the charges involved, but this is constant in the case of the hydrogen atom, so we need not consider it.)

In the hydrogen atom (as, indeed, in any atom) there is an attractive force between the electron and the positively charged nucleus. If the electron is to move away from the nucleus, energy will have to be supplied to overcome this attractive force. If the electron now moves back to its original position, exactly the same amount of energy will be released as was supplied in the first step. (This follows from the law of the conservation of energy, which you met in Unit 9.) One of the ways in which release of energy can manifest itself is emission of electromagnetic radiation. Similarly, absorption of electromagnetic radiation means that energy is being absorbed.

With this in mind, let us now look at the emission spectrum of the hydrogen atom. The visible part of the spectrum consists of just four sharp lines (Spectrum B on the colour plate.)

> What does Spectrum B tell you about the energy changes possible for the hydrogen atom?

(i) *Spectrum B contains a very limited number of frequencies* in comparison with Spectrum A, the continuous spectrum. Only four visible frequencies appear, whereas in the continuous spectrum all possible frequencies are represented. A limited number of emission frequencies testifies to a limited number of energy changes of the electron in the atom. You should remember from Section 6.2 of Unit 10 how energy and frequency are related by the equation

$$E = hf \tag{9}$$

where h is Planck's constant $\approx 6.626 \times 10^{-34}$ J s, and f is expressed in hertz (or s^{-1}), and E in joules.

(ii) *The sharpness of the lines shows that the energy changes are very specific in size.*

It would be nice to know if the spectrum continues beyond the range our eyes can see. Luckily, photographic film has a wider range of sensitivity than the human eye and can 'see' into both the ultraviolet and infrared. If, instead of just looking down the spectroscope, we take a photograph of the spectrum, we find that the series of emission lines continues into the ultraviolet, but not the infrared. Figure 17 indicates the spectrum that can be obtained in such a photograph. This series of lines, which was first studied by the physicist Johann Balmer in the late nineteenth century, is called the Balmer series. You will have an opportunity to study this spectrum yourself at Summer School.

FIGURE 17   The Balmer series in the atomic spectrum of hydrogen. This emission spectrum and all subsequent spectra in these Units are depicted as black lines on a white background. In practice, photographs of *emission* spectra appear as white lines on a black background.

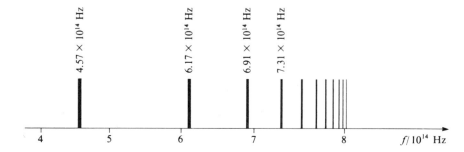

□ What do you notice about the spacing of the lines in this series?

■ They get closer together at higher energy. (We shall return to this observation in Section 5.4.)

Table 5 lists the frequencies at which the first seven lines of the spectrum in Figure 17 are observed. We have also listed the energy changes of the atom, which are equal to the corresponding photon energies.

SAQ 17   Use Spectrum B to make an estimate of the energy change corresponding to the red emission line in the spectrum of the hydrogen atom.

If you had any trouble with SAQ 17, make sure you follow the working of this calculation for the blue–green line (given below Table 5).

TABLE 5   Frequencies and energy changes for the lines in the Balmer series of hydrogen

Line	Colour	Frequency/10^{14} Hz (or s^{-1})	Energy change/10^{-19} J
1	red	4.57	
2	blue–green	6.17	4.09
3	violet	6.91	4.58
4	dark violet	7.31	4.84
5	ultraviolet	7.55	5.00
6	ultraviolet	7.71	5.11
7	ultraviolet	7.81	5.17

Blue–green line: $E = hf$, where h is Planck's constant

$$h \approx 6.626 \times 10^{-34}\,\text{J s}$$

$$f = 6.17 \times 10^{14}\,\text{Hz (or s}^{-1})$$

$$E = (6.626 \times 10^{-34}\,\text{J s}) \times (6.17 \times 10^{14}\,\text{s}^{-1})$$

$$= 4.09 \times 10^{-19}\,\text{J}$$

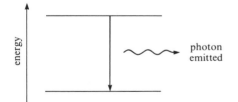

FIGURE 18   The emission of a photon represented by an electron jump between two energy levels.

5.2 THE ENERGY-LEVEL DIAGRAM

The simple pattern in Figure 17 invites a simple explanation. You already know that the energy changes permitted to an electron in the hydrogen atom are sharply defined, and that each line in the emission spectrum is the result of an electron 'jump' from higher to lower energy. This strongly suggests that the electron energies in the atom are themselves sharply defined. We can represent the electron energies on a diagram as **energy levels**. In such a diagram, an electron jump is shown as an arrow from one level to another, downwards for emission (Figure 18) because the energy of the electron decreases.

If we assume that all the electron jumps responsible for the spectral lines in Figure 17 terminate at the same lower level, the spectrum is easily interpreted. We can take this level as a baseline and arbitrarily give it zero energy, and then, by measuring each of the jumps from this reference point, build up a diagram of electron energy levels in the hydrogen atom.

EXERCISE I

On Figure 19, draw horizontal lines to represent the energy levels involved in the spectrum shown in Figure 17. Take as your scale $1\,\text{cm} = 1 \times 10^{-19}\,\text{J}$ (and use a sharp pencil!). The data for drawing the energy levels are in Table 5. Make sure that you have answered SAQ 17 and completed Table 5. For reasons that will become clearer later, you should mark the base level 18 cm from the bottom of the Figure. The next level should be drawn at a position corresponding to $3.03 \times 10^{-19}\,\text{J}$ (that is, approximately 3 cm) above this base level, then another at $4.09 \times 10^{-19}\,\text{J}$ above the baseline, and so on, using the data in Table 5. This diagram is called an **electron energy-level diagram**.

It is now an easy matter to represent on your diagram the electron jumps or 'transitions' producing the emission spectrum of Figure 17. From each level in the diagram draw a downward-pointing arrow terminating at the base level. This indicates the loss in energy when the electron jumps to this level from a higher one. (Try not to fill up more than the left-hand third of the page with arrows at this stage: you will be using the rest of the diagram in later Sections.) The top left corner of your diagram should now look like Figure 61 on p. 82.

SAQ 18   What would be the energy of the photon emitted if an electron jumped between the highest level of Figure 19 and the second lowest?

5.3 THE LYMAN SERIES

It is not surprising that the first series of spectral lines observed for the hydrogen atom lay at least partly in the visible region of the electromagnetic spectrum. The visible lines cannot fail to be noticed by anyone who investigates the spectrum of atomic hydrogen. But before we conclude that an electron energy-level diagram based on this series offers a complete description of the hydrogen atom's electronic energies, it would be wise to look in other spectral regions for other possible series.

> If the hydrogen atom has more energy levels, apart from those shown in Figure 19, in which spectral region would you expect to find evidence for this?

The spectral lines in Figure 17 are getting closer and closer together with increasing frequency, suggesting that the higher electron energy levels also converge. To fit in extra levels in Figure 19 at energies far higher than all the others would break the pattern of converging lines. But it would be quite possible to imagine other *lower* energy levels. If there are energy levels below the lowest one drawn on Figure 19, we would expect spectral lines resulting from transitions that terminate on the new level(s) to lie in the ultraviolet.

☐ Why would these spectral lines lie in the ultraviolet?

■ Because the energy differences between higher energy levels and any new, low one are larger than any shown so far on Figure 19, the frequencies of corresponding spectral lines must be higher than those in the visible range.

In fact, investigation of the ultraviolet region shows that there is another series of lines in the hydrogen spectrum, which lies in the region from $2 \times 10^{15}\,\text{Hz}$ to $3.5 \times 10^{15}\,\text{Hz}$. These lines are produced by transitions to a level that lies $16.34 \times 10^{-19}\,\text{J}$ *below* the lowest level you have previously drawn in Figure 19. (You should now include this line on your energy-level diagram.) A survey of the far ultraviolet and X-ray region fails to reveal any other series of lines due to atomic hydrogen, so the level you have just drawn in Figure 19 is, in fact, the *lowest* energy level in the hydrogen atom.

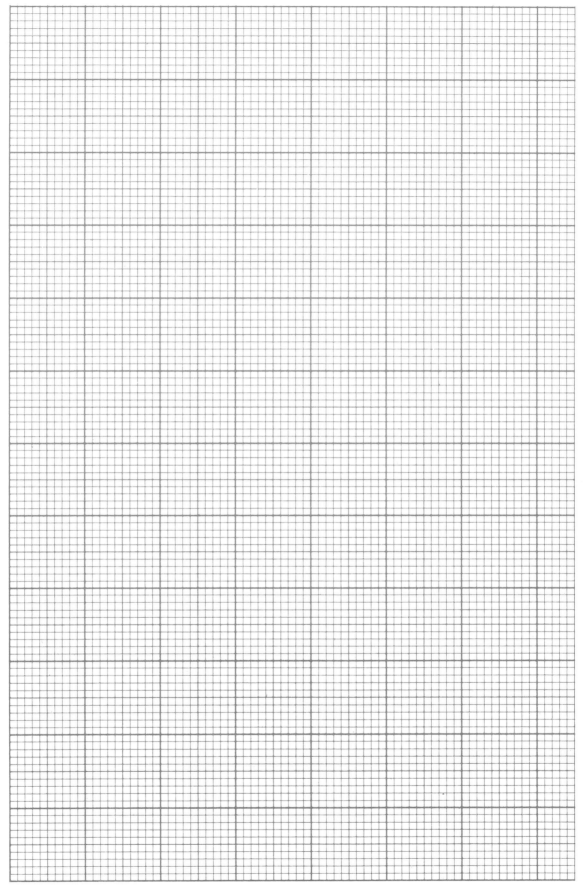

FIGURE 19   Your energy-level diagram for the hydrogen atom.

PRINCIPAL QUANTUM
NUMBER, *n*

GROUND STATE OF AN
ATOM

EXCITED STATE OF AN
ATOM

CONTINUUM

CONTINUUM LEVEL

IONIZATION ENERGY, *I*

Now that you have a complete picture of the energy levels in the hydrogen atom, it is useful to be able to refer to them. Label the lowest level 1. Succeeding energy levels can then be numbered, for convenience, 2, 3, 4, etc. The number given to any particular level is known as its **principal quantum number**, and is given the symbol *n*, where *n* can equal 1, 2, 3, 4, . . . etc.

In a hydrogen atom the single electron is usually to be found in the lowest possible level ($n = 1$). This corresponds to the **ground state** of the atom. The electron can occupy one of the higher energy levels only if the extra energy for this has been obtained from some other source. This source could be a photon, or the kinetic energy of the electrons or ions in an electric discharge (like the one in a fluorescent tube). When energy is absorbed by an atom, an electron is transferred to an electron energy level higher than the lowest level, and we say that the atom is 'excited' or in an **excited state**. This means that a hydrogen atom in which the electron is in any of the higher levels, $n = 2, 3, 4$, etc., of Figure 19, is in an excited state.

The series of lines corresponding to transitions between the various higher levels and the lowest ($n = 1$) level is called the Lyman series, after its discovery by Theodore Lyman in 1906.

Other series are also named after their discoverers; for example, the series with lower level $n = 3$ is called the Paschen series. You should now complete Figure 19 by including the series of arrows representing the Lyman and Paschen series. It would make the diagram clearer if you use a different coloured pencil for each of the three series.

Your diagram should now look like Figure 62 on p. 83.

☐ Do you expect any series of hydrogen emission lines to lie in the infrared?

■ Yes: any series terminating in levels higher than $n = 2$ will have energies lower than that of visible radiation.

Figure 20 shows the complete emission spectrum of the hydrogen atom. If you look closely, you will see that there is some overlap between the series in the infrared corresponding to transitions terminating at $n = 3$, $n = 4$, $n = 5$, etc.

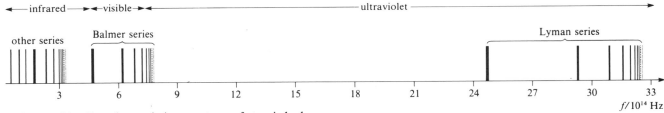

FIGURE 20   Complete emission spectrum of atomic hydrogen.

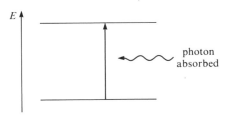

FIGURE 21   An absorption represented by a transition between two energy levels.

☐ Remember the discussion of absorption spectra in Section 5. How would you represent the process of absorption on your energy-level diagram?

■ When an atom absorbs energy, an electron jumps to a higher energy level. This is represented by an upward-pointing arrow, as shown in Figure 21. Figure 22 shows the Lyman series in absorption. It is produced when hydrogen atoms absorb particular frequencies from continuous radiation in the far ultraviolet region of the spectrum.

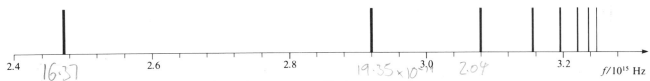

FIGURE 22   The Lyman series as an absorption spectrum of hydrogen.

SAQ 19   Use Figure 19 and Table 5 to predict the frequencies of the three lowest-frequency absorption lines in the Lyman series. Which energy levels are involved in each transition?

5.4 IONIZATION ENERGY

Your electron energy-level diagram (Figure 19) summarizes our knowledge of the behaviour of the electron in the hydrogen atom:

1   It emphasizes the fact that the energy of the electron in the atom can only have certain values, which we label with whole numbers, called quantum numbers. We say that the electron energy is 'quantized'.

2   It indicates these allowed values of the energy relative to the lowest level (with principal quantum number $n = 1$), which is arbitrarily given the value zero, that is $E_1 = 0$.

3   It shows how the electron can jump between allowed levels, absorbing or emitting photons of electromagnetic radiation.

4   The energy of the photon emitted or absorbed is, of course, equal to the energy difference between the levels concerned.

One other property of the diagram will have forced itself to your attention (particularly if your pencil was blunt!): the energy levels get closer together at higher energy. Eventually, they converge to a limit. Above this limit the electron may have any energy. This continuous range of energy is called the **continuum** of energy. The energy at which it starts is called the **continuum level**.

We can illustrate the situation graphically by plotting E_n, the energy of the level labelled n (measured from the $n = 1$ level; assuming $E_1 = 0$) against the principal quantum number n.

EXERCISE 2

On Figure 23, plot energy E_n against principal quantum number n, using a scale $1\,\text{cm} = 1 \times 10^{-19}\,\text{J}$. The first two points are shown. Complete the graph as far as $n = 9$ using data from Table 5. Remember to add $16.34 \times 10^{-19}\,\text{J}$ to each of the energies in Table 5, because in this exercise you are assuming $E_1 = 0$. You should find when you join up the points that they lie on a smooth curve.

Extend the graph beyond $n = 9$ by continuing the line of the curve. (This process of extending a graph beyond the measured data is called *extrapolation* (*MAFS* 3)). Remember, though, that only integral values of n have any physical significance. Now estimate a value of E_n for (i) $n = 10$, and (ii) $n = 12$.
Our estimates for these two energies were very similar.

What does this mean?

There is an upper limit to the energy an electron can have in an atom. If the electron is given more energy than this limiting value, it escapes from the atom. The electron is no longer bound to the nucleus and its energy is no longer quantized. If an atom absorbs a photon with more energy than is needed to remove the electron from the atom, the excess takes the form of kinetic energy, that is, energy of motion of the electron away from the nucleus. The energy of an electron that is not bound to the nucleus is represented by a value that lies in the continuum of energy.

The minimum energy required to remove an electron from an atom originally in its ground state is known as the **ionization energy**, I, of that atom. As you will see in later Units, ionization energy is a quantity of considerable importance in understanding atomic structure and in chemistry generally.

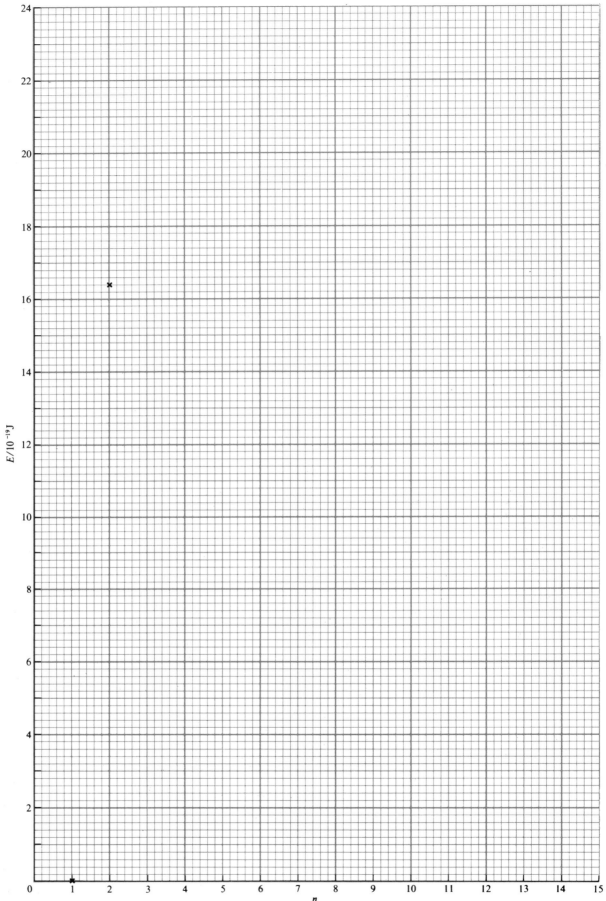

FIGURE 23   Your plot to estimate the ionization energy of hydrogen.

As the final part of Exercise 2, estimate the ionization energy of hydrogen from Figure 23. Then estimate an uncertainty in the value as follows. Estimate the highest and lowest value of the ionization energy of hydrogen that you could obtain by extrapolating the data in Figure 23. Using these estimates, within what uncertainty limits are you confident that the true answer lies?

Now look back to Figure 22, which shows the complete absorption spectrum of atomic hydrogen. Here you can see the absorption lines getting closer and closer at higher energies. Eventually they will merge into a continuum. If we can estimate the frequency at which continuous absorption commences, we can easily find out how much energy is needed to remove the electron from a hydrogen atom in its ground state.

ITQ 3 Estimate where this continuum occurs by inspection of Figure 22. Check that this is in reasonable agreement with your extrapolation in Figure 23.

Enter here your estimate of the frequency at which the continuum starts.

Frequency, $f =$

Energy, $hf =$

Uncertainty limits $\pm$

Although the value of the ionization energy obtained from Figure 22 should agree within experimental uncertainty with that obtained in Exercise 2, the uncertainties are rather large. Other graphical procedures are available that give more accurate values of ionization energy from spectra. You will meet these at Summer School. For our present purposes, however, the value you have just obtained is sufficiently accurate.

SAQ 20 Can the ground-state hydrogen atom absorb a photon with an energy of: (i) 21.34×10^{-19} J; (ii) 22.74×10^{-19} J; (iii) 17.5×10^{-19} J; (iv) 11.0×10^{-19} J?

5.5 OTHER ATOMS

In Section 5 we have come quite a long way towards understanding the hydrogen atom. We have satisfactorily explained its spectrum and obtained some very significant quantitative information, the ionization energy. But how far does our knowledge of what the electron is doing in the hydrogen atom help us to understand other atoms? How far can we extend this treatment?

Without making matters much more complicated, we can look at the spectra of the ions He^+ and Li^{2+}, which, like the hydrogen atom, contain only *one* electron. Figures 24 and 25 illustrate the highest-energy series of spectral lines for each of these ions.

> How do these spectra (a) resemble and (b) differ from the Lyman series of the hydrogen atom?

The patterns of lines in Figures 24 and 25 are simple, and reminiscent of the pattern we saw in Figure 22. However, the energy changes giving rise to the He^+ spectrum are much larger than those obtained for similar transitions

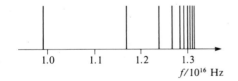

FIGURE 24   The Lyman series for He^+.

FIGURE 25   The Lyman series for Li^{2+}.

35

SUCCESSIVE IONIZATION
ENERGIES

in the H atom. Transition energies for Li^{2+} are larger again, the spectrum obtained falling around the boundary between far ultraviolet and X-ray radiation.

The spectra show that He^+ and Li^{2+} are like the hydrogen atom in that the electron can only be accommodated in specific energy levels. They also show that similarly labelled levels do not have the same energy in each atom. The $n = 2$ level, for example, lies 6.54×10^{-18} J above the lowest level ($n = 1$) in He^+, and 14.7×10^{-18} J above the lowest level in Li^{2+}. The corresponding energy difference for H is 1.634×10^{-18} J.

When an atom has more than one electron, you may expect the situation to become more complex. Even if we restrict our attention to the energy jumps of one particular electron, it becomes necessary to consider the interaction of this electron with other electrons as well as the simple electron–nucleus interaction, which describes one-electron atoms. A consequence of this is that we get many more electron energy levels and it rapidly becomes increasingly difficult to disentangle the various overlapping series of lines that result.

However, a glance at Figure 26 (Na) and Spectrum D (He) on the colour plate shows that regularities are apparent in at least certain parts of the spectra of many-electron atoms. On the other hand, some spectra (Spectra J and L on the colour plate) are so highly complex that their interpretation is a major task, even for the specialist.

FIGURE 26   Part of the absorption spectrum of sodium.

SUMMARY OF SECTION 5

1   The nuclear model of the atom envisages a small but massive nucleus consisting of protons and neutrons. The positive charge of the nucleus is balanced by the negative charge of the electrons, which occupy the relatively vast regions of space around nuclei.

2   Atoms absorb and emit radiation of certain 'permitted' frequencies, which are characteristic of each type of atom. Since the energy of an atom can only change by the energies of the photons that the atom absorbs or emits, we infer that atoms can only have certain 'permitted' energies. The transitions between the permitted energies of the hydrogen atom are interpreted as jumps of the electron between different allowed electron energy levels, which are labelled with the principal quantum number, n; n has integral values, beginning with $n = 1$ for the lowest level.

3   The electron in hydrogen normally occupies the lowest level, and the atom is in the ground state. The electron energy levels get closer together at higher energy and eventually converge to a level called the continuum level. Above this level, the energy of the electron is not quantized and the levels form a continuous band of energies, the continuum. An electron excited into the continuum is no longer bound by the atom; the atom is ionized.

4   Atoms with more than one electron produce more complex spectra with overlapping series of lines, although for some atoms, series can be recognized in the spectra.

SAQ 21   In an experiment, an emission line in the spectrum of hydrogen is observed to have a frequency of approximately 1.6×10^{14} Hz. Which transition is responsible for this emission line?

(Hint   Refer to your completed Figure 19; Planck's constant is approximately 6.6×10^{-34} J s.)

SAQ 22 What is the energy of the $n = 1$ to $n = 7$ transition for (i) H, (ii) He$^+$, (iii) Li^{2+}?

SAQ 23 Can you suggest a reason why the electron in He$^+$ should be more tightly held than that in H, and the Li^{2+} electron should be more strongly held than that in He$^+$?

6 SHELLS, SUBSHELLS AND THE SECOND QUANTUM NUMBER

The interpretation of the spectra of atoms that contain more than one electron is quite complicated. Fortunately, we can obtain a great deal of information about the arrangement of electrons in an atom by measuring the energy required to *remove* electrons from atoms. In this Section we shall examine how such measurements can lead us to the need for a second quantum number to describe electrons in atoms, and so provide a more complete description of atoms.

☐ Can you recall the name given to the minimum energy required to remove an electron from an atom in its ground state?

■ The minimum energy required to remove an electron from an atom in its ground state is called the ionization energy. In Section 5 you saw how ionization energies can be measured by spectroscopy, from the continuum level in the electron energy-level diagram.

Consider an atom of sodium. Its atomic number is 11, so there are 11 electrons in the atom. Suppose that we could remove all these electrons *one at a time*.

Would you expect the energies required to remove each of these 11 electrons in turn to be the same? What is the reason for your answer?

After one electron is removed, the atom contains 10 electrons and a nucleus with 11 positive charges. The atom now carries a net positive charge. It follows that the second electron will be more difficult to remove than the first because the negatively charged electron is held more strongly by the atom. You might expect that the energy needed to remove successive electrons would increase, perhaps in some regular way. These energies are called **successive ionization energies**.* Table 6 lists the successive ionization energies for sodium.

A plot of these values reveals a pattern more clearly than the Table does. Figure 27 shows that each successive electron requires more energy to remove it.

What striking or surprising features do you observe in this figure?

It is obvious that the successive ionization energies do not increase in a regular way, although there appears to be a pattern in the values. Thus, the first electron is much more easily removed than subsequent ones. The energy needed to remove each of the next eight electrons increases gradually but not very regularly. The last two electrons are held very tightly in the atom. Apparently, the electrons in sodium fall into three groups. The first electron removed is in a different group from the next eight, and the last two electrons make the third group. How are we to interpret these groupings?

TABLE 6 Successive ionization energies of sodium/10^{-19} J

first	8.23
second	75.76
third	114.78
fourth	158.47
fifth	221.72
sixth	275.82
seventh	334.01
eighth	423.27
ninth	480.45
tenth	2 347.36
eleventh	2 641.47

* Successive ionization energies can be measured by a technique you have encountered in a different context, mass spectrometry. By steadily increasing the energy of the electron beam, the energy required to produce successively charged ions can be measured. Normally, these energies are measured in electronvolts (eV), but for ease of comparison of energies, we have converted them into joules in Table 6 ($1\,eV \approx 1.602 \times 10^{-19}$ J).

PHOTOELECTRON SPECTROSCOPY

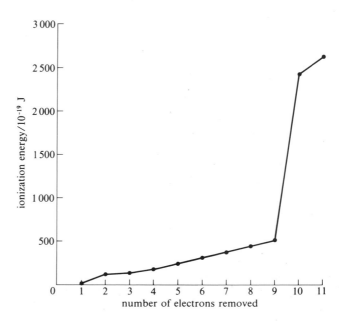

FIGURE 27   Successive ionization energies of sodium.

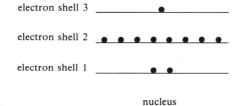

electron shell 3

electron shell 2

electron shell 1

nucleus

FIGURE 28   Electron energy shells for sodium.

The electron that is most easily removed is bound to the atom by a relatively small force. On the other hand, the last two electrons removed are the most firmly bound. You will recall that the Coulomb law describes the relationship between the force that attracts two oppositely charged bodies and the distance separating them. The law implies that the most loosely bound electron is relatively far from the nucleus. This is the outermost electron. The two most tightly bound electrons are relatively close to the nucleus, the innermost electrons. As Figure 28 shows, we can imagine the electrons (which are represented by spots) being contained in *shells* at various distances from a central nucleus.

In Figure 28 the electrons with the highest ionization energy (the most tightly bound) are shown at the bottom of the Figure. It is a convention to place the most tightly bound electrons at the bottom of this sort of diagram, and we shall adopt it throughout the rest of Units 11–12. But notice that it inverts the grouping of electrons that we recognized in Figure 27.

Figure 27 reveals an important property of electrons in atoms—a property that you have already deduced from the appearance of *line* spectra of atoms in Section 5.

Can you detect what this property is?

As the Figure shows, ionization energies have specific values, indicating that the electrons in atoms can only have certain 'permitted' energies. Using the spectrum of hydrogen in Section 5, you were able to construct an electron energy-level diagram for hydrogen, which you labelled with the principal quantum number, n. If the electron shells are numbered, starting with 1 for the innermost shell as in Figure 28, then these numbers correspond to the same principal quantum numbers that you used for the energy levels in the hydrogen atom. The correspondence between shells and energy levels will become apparent shortly.

The successive ionization energies of atoms of other elements reveal the same type of shell structure of the electrons as in sodium. The first shell is found to contain, at most, two electrons and the second shell contains, at most, eight electrons. In this way the successive ionization energies provide a simple though approximate picture of the electron energy levels within atoms.

However, ionization energies are expected to increase as the charge on the ion increases (Coulomb's law). So the removal of successive electrons does not readily reveal whether each of the electrons within an electron shell is held with the same energy in the atom, or why the first shell contains two electrons and the second shell up to eight electrons. It seems that we cannot easily refine the electron shell model depicted in Figure 28 using values of successive ionization energies.

We are however, able to use the results of another type of spectroscopy—**photoelectron spectroscopy**—which provides direct information on energy levels by allowing us in a way to 'see' energy levels in atoms. Before examining the results of photoelectron spectroscopy, we need to consider how this kind of experiment provides this information.

In Section 5 you saw that when hydrogen atoms are irradiated with ultra-violet radiation they absorb radiation of certain frequencies corresponding to the differences between energy levels in the atom.

□ Look back to Figure 19. What would you expect to happen when a hydrogen atom in its ground state absorbs radiation with photon energy $E = hf = 40 \times 10^{-19} \, \text{J}$?

■ The ionization energy, I, of a hydrogen atom is less than this energy ($I = 21.78 \times 10^{-19} \, \text{J}$). Remember that when an atom absorbs a photon with energy higher than the ionization energy of the atom, the atom is ionized: an electron is ejected from the atom. As you know from Unit 10, the electron emitted when a substance is irradiated with photons is called a *photoelectron*.

□ Where will the excess energy appear?

■ As the photon is absorbed, the photon energy hf is used to increase the separation of the electron and the nucleus. The excess energy will appear as kinetic energy of the electron and nucleus as they move apart. Practically all of this excess energy will belong to the photoelectron because the nucleus, being much more massive than the electron, remains effectively stationary.

Write an expression for the kinetic energy, E_k, of the photoelectron, in terms of the photon energy hf and the ionization energy I.

The expression you have written should be familiar. As you know from the description of the photoelectric effect in Unit 10, electrons are emitted when the frequency of the radiation is equal to or greater than some threshold frequency, that is when the photon energy exceeds some critical value. According to the law of the conservation of energy, the kinetic energy of the photoelectron is just the difference between the photon energy, hf, and this threshold energy, I:

$$E_k = hf - I \tag{10}$$

As you see from Equation 10, photoionization from gaseous atoms is similar in principle to photoelectron emission from a solid metal. The same relationship applies to each process. Equation 10 also shows that if we know the photon energy, and if we can measure the kinetic energy of the electrons, we can determine the ionization energy of the atom. The relationship between the terms in the photoelectric equation is more apparent if it is represented diagrammatically, as in Figure 29, which shows the ionization energy as the difference in energy between the continuum level and the electron energy level. This relationship between ionization energy and the kinetic energy of the photoelectron is the basis of photoelectron spectroscopy.

The results of photoelectron spectroscopy turn out to be much more useful than those from successive ionization energies, because in photoelectron spectroscopy we can measure the energy required to remove *each* electron from the *uncharged atom* instead of successive electrons from the increasingly charged *ion*.

Although the technique is simple in principle, it is quite complex in practice. To obtain a 'spectrum' of photoelectron energies we first require a source of photons that all have the same energy (or frequency). Radiation of just one frequency is called monochromatic radiation. With such a source of radi-

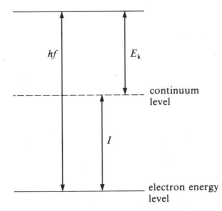

FIGURE 29   The relationship between I, E_k and hf.

BOUND STATE

UNBOUND ELECTRON

ation, the photon energy, *hf*, in Equation 10 is fixed. All that remains is to determine the kinetic energy of the photoelectrons that are ejected from the atoms.

Can you suggest a means of doing this? Remember that photoelectrons, like ions, have charge and mass (albeit very small).

In the photoelectron experiment we shine monochromatic radiation on atoms. A photon can cause the emission of one of a number of electrons in an atom, *provided that the photon energy hf is greater than the ionization energy I of that electron.* So when the beam of photons irradiates the sample of atoms, photoelectrons are produced from many atoms and from different shells within these atoms. These photoelectrons have kinetic energies that depend on the photon energy, which is the same for all the photoionizations, and on the ionization energy, which depends on the electron that is emitted. The kinetic energies of the photoelectrons are determined in a similar way to the determination of the kinetic energies of ions in a mass spectrometer (see Section 2.2.1). From the kinetic energies of the photoelectrons it is a simple matter to calculate the ionization energies using Equation 10. A plot of the number of photoelectrons detected versus the ionization energy is called a photoelectron spectrum.

In this way the energy levels of electrons in atoms can be examined directly; each peak in a photoelectron spectrum corresponds to ionization of an electron from an electron energy level. Figure 30 shows the simple relationship between the photoelectron spectrum of an atom with three occupied electron energy levels and the electron energy-level diagram for that atom. Notice that when the spectrum is rotated through 90° it gives a picture of the electron energy-level diagram. Notice too that the most *tightly* bound electrons (those with the highest ionization energies) occupy the lowest energy levels in the atom.

Photoelectron spectroscopy contrasts with the atomic spectroscopic technique you used in Section 5. In atomic spectra each line in the spectrum represents the difference between two **bound states** of the electron in the atom. Photoelectron spectroscopy measures the difference between a bound state of the electron and the energy of an **unbound electron** at the continuum level.

Since we are interested in investigating the electron energy levels of atoms, we shall mainly restrict our attention to elements that exist conveniently (at ordinary temperatures) as separate atoms, and not substances that consist of combinations of atoms. These monatomic gases are minor components

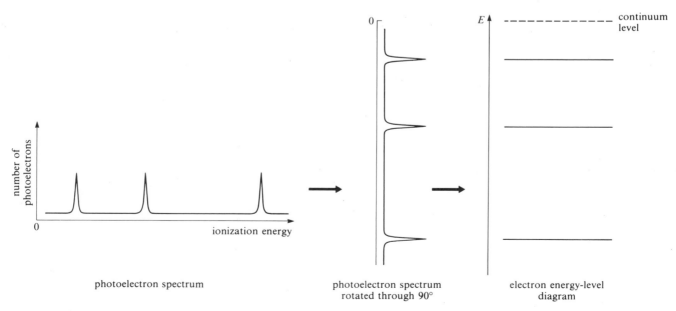

photoelectron spectrum

photoelectron spectrum
rotated through 90°

electron energy-level
diagram

FIGURE 30 The relationship of the electron energy-level diagram to the photoelectron spectrum. The presence of a peak in the photoelectron spectrum indicates the emission of electrons with a particular ionization energy.

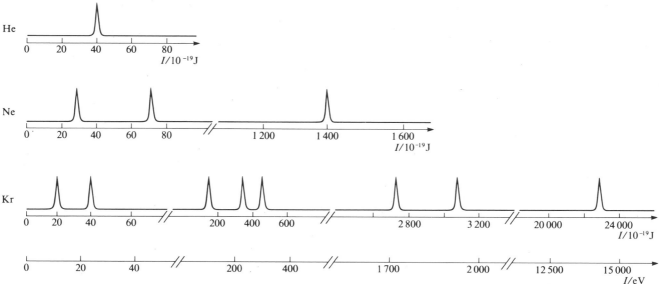

FIGURE 31 The photoelectron spectra of helium, neon and krypton: notice how the scales are broken and that large energy gaps occur between the electron shells.

of the atmosphere—helium, neon, argon, krypton and xenon, the noble gases. The photoelectron spectra of three noble gases, helium, neon and krypton, are shown schematically in Figure 31. In these spectra, as in all the photoelectron spectra in these Units, the peaks are shown as having equal intensities. In fact the intensities of the peaks in a spectrum will not be the same, because they depend on the number of electrons of a particular energy and on the likelihood of photoemission. To ionize the tightly bound electrons in neon and krypton, radiation consisting of photons of very high energy is needed. We use X-rays. The energy scale for the krypton spectrum in Figure 31 is graduated in electronvolts as well as the more familiar energy unit, the joule. In this type of experiment, results are conventionally reported in electronvolts, since this is the kinetic energy acquired by an electron that has been accelerated by a potential difference of one volt. However, for easy comparison with other electron energy diagrams in these Units, we shall plot photoelectron spectra in joules.

To interpret these spectra you will need to know how many electrons are contained in each type of atom.

☐ Where can you find this information?

■ Remember that the number of electrons is equal to the atomic number, and these are listed in Appendix 1.

Complete the Table in the margin using the values of the atomic numbers.

Obviously a lot of information is contained in the spectra in Figure 31. Concentrate on the most obvious features. Look first at the spectrum of helium.

How many electron energy levels do the two electrons occupy in a helium atom?

The helium spectrum contains only one peak. This implies that each of the two electrons in helium has the same ionization energy: both electrons occupy the same electron energy level in the atom. It is convenient to represent this diagrammatically, denoting electron energy levels by a line as you did in Section 5 and electrons by circles. Figure 32 represents a helium atom in its ground state. Notice that the electron energy level is labelled $n = 1$ in Figure 32. In helium, as in hydrogen, the electrons in the ground state occupy the lowest electron energy level, which has principal quantum number $n = 1$.

It is apparent from Figure 32 that more than one electron can occupy the electron energy level $n = 1$. This raises some questions. How many electrons can occupy a given level? Why do two electrons occupy the same level in helium? We shall be returning to these questions shortly.

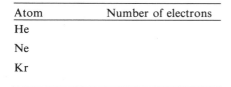

Atom	Number of electrons
He	
Ne	
Kr	

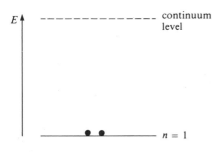

FIGURE 32 The electron energy-level diagram of helium.

ELECTRON SHELL

ELECTRON SUBSHELL

SECOND QUANTUM
NUMBER, l

Now look again at the three spectra in Figure 31. Other obvious features
are:

1   The spectra of neon and krypton contain more than one peak.

2   The number of peaks increases with atomic number, that is with the
number of electrons.

3   Within a spectrum the peaks fall into groups, each of which spans a
relatively small range in the values of I (by less than a factor of three), for
example the three peaks in the range 150 to 450×10^{-19} J in the krypton
spectrum. On the other hand, the energy differences between groups are
considerably larger.

Using the energy-level model that we developed in Section 5, how can
you account for the first two points above?

The number of peaks in the photoelectron spectrum of an atom (that is, the
number of different ionization energies) is equal to the number of occupied
energy levels in the atom. Apparently, the number of levels that are
occupied increases with the number of electrons. The most plausible explanation of this observation is that there is a limit to the number of electrons
that can occupy any level, and as electrons are added they occupy higher
levels. This explanation is consistent with the shell interpretation of the
successive ionization energies of sodium (Figure 28).

This shell interpretation is reflected in the grouping or pattern of electron
energy levels. In neon, for example, there are three peaks, which are divided
into two groups: one peak at high I ($1\,390 \times 10^{-19}$ J) and two peaks at low
I (less than 80×10^{-19} J). You have seen in Section 5 a relationship
between the energy of an electron and its distance from the nucleus. The
electron most easily removed is held with the smallest force because it is
furthest from the nucleus. Conversely, the electron most tightly bound is
closest to the nucleus and has a high ionization energy. This introduces the
idea of inner and outer groups of electrons in neon. We call these groups
electron shells, as we did with the electron energy-level diagram for Na, and
we number them from the nucleus outwards starting at 1. Figure 33 shows
how the shells are labelled for neon. In fact these numbers *are* the principal
quantum numbers that you used to label the energy levels derived from the
spectrum of hydrogen. The relationship between the photoelectron spectra
in Figures 31 and 33 and an electron energy-level diagram is again immediately obvious if you turn the page through 90° so that the spectra are
arranged vertically with the $n = 1$ level at the bottom and $I = 0$ at the top.

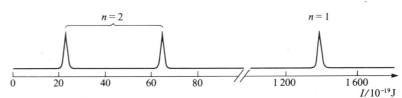

FIGURE 33   Electron shells in neon, as shown by its photoelectron spectrum.

ITQ 4   Now draw an energy-level diagram for krypton, based on its
photoelectron spectrum (Figure 31) and label it with the principal quantum
numbers, n.

Viewed as electron energy-level diagrams, the spectra in Figure 31 show
that, roughly speaking, these atoms have a pattern of energy levels similar
to hydrogen, although in hydrogen only the lowest level ($n = 1$) is occupied
in the ground state. But notice that electrons in the inner shells are more
tightly held as the atomic number increases. This is exactly what we would
expect because the nuclear charge is directly proportional to the atomic
number.

Another difference is apparent if you compare the spectra in Figure 31 with the energy-level diagram for hydrogen (Figure 19).

What is this difference?

In hydrogen each of the quantum numbers describes a *single* electron energy level. As the photoelectron spectra show, this is not true for other atoms. The electron shells consist of a number of electron energy levels, which we call **electron subshells**. The spectrum of krypton gives us some information about these subshells.

How many subshells are there in each of the electron shells $n = 1$ to $n = 3$?

$n = 1$, number of subshells = ?

$n = 2$, number of subshells = ?

$n = 3$, number of subshells = ?

For these three electron shells there appears to be a relationship between the number of subshells and the principal quantum number, but you may be wondering why Figure 31 does not show *four* subshells in the electron shell $n = 4$. In fact there are four, but in krypton only *two* of these subshells contain electrons; the other two are empty. So we have a simple rule, derived from the photoelectron spectra, but which can also be established theoretically. *The number of subshells in any electron shell is equal to the principal quantum number of that electron shell.*

In Section 5 we introduced the principal quantum number as a means of labelling the electron energy levels in hydrogen. The value of n describes completely the electron energy level occupied by an electron in hydrogen, but it fails to do this for all other atoms. To describe the subshell structure we need a **second quantum number**. This quantum number is given the symbol l. Strictly, this quantum number is called the orbital angular momentum quantum number, but in these Units we shall call it the second quantum number.

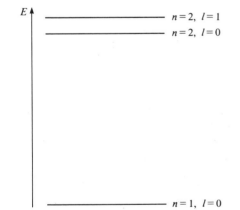

Like the principal quantum number, l is given values corresponding to the energy of the subshell, but for theoretical reasons that are beyond the scope of these Units the lowest value that l is given is zero. So for any particular shell, the subshells are numbered from zero to $(n - 1)$.

☐ What are the possible values that l can have for the third and fourth electron shells?

■ For $n = 3$, l can have values 0, 1 and 2. There are three subshells, as you saw in the spectrum of krypton. For $n = 4$, l can have values 0, 1, 2 and 3. There are four subshells, although in krypton only the first two of these are occupied, that is $l = 0$ and $l = 1$.

FIGURE 34 The electron energy-level diagram for neon, showing the levels labelled by quantum numbers n and l (not to scale).

Notice that the lowest value of l is given to the subshell with the lowest energy. Thus, in neon the levels can be labelled as in Figure 34. Of course, this diagram reflects exactly the electron energy levels that are revealed by photoelectron spectroscopy (Figure 31).

Implicit in the observation that the number of occupied levels or subshells increases with atomic number is the idea that electrons fill the lowest electron energy levels first. You would, of course, expect atoms to adopt the most stable arrangement, with their electrons in the lowest electron energy levels. Since you also know the number of subshells (l value) in any shell (any value of n), you have almost enough information to draw a diagram showing which levels the electrons occupy—but not quite.

☐ What further information do you need?

■ So far we have said very little about the *number* of electrons that can occupy each level.

It is not easy to determine how many electrons can be contained in each particular level using information from photoelectron spectroscopy. It can be established from a mathematical model of the atom such as that used to obtain Figure 13. However, you already have a clue to the number of electrons that can be accommodated in any level. Look at Figure 28, which shows the electron energy shells of sodium.

How many electrons can be accommodated in the electron shells

$n = 1$?

$n = 2$?

There are 2 (in $n = 1$) and 8 (in $n = 2$). Remember that in sodium the $n = 3$ shell is not full. Now from Figure 34 you can also see that the $n = 2$ electron shell is divided into two subshells, $l = 0$ and $l = 1$. Since the single shell in helium ($n = 1$, $l = 0$) holds two electrons, it seems reasonable to suppose that the $n = 2$, $l = 0$ subshell in sodium also holds a maximum of two electrons. In fact, all subshells with $l = 0$ can hold a maximum of two electrons.

☐ Now complete the following table by writing the maximum number of electrons in each of the subshells in the first two electron shells.

Shell	Subshell	Number of electrons that can be accommodated
$n = 1$	$l = 0$	
$n = 2$	$l = 0$	
$n = 2$	$l = 1$	

■ The missing numbers are, respectively, 2, 2 and 6.

ITQ 5   Now complete Figure 34 by drawing in the dots to represent electrons in neon, in the same way as in Figure 32. An atom of neon contains 10 electrons.

The subshells with $l = 0$ can each accommodate two electrons, and the subshells with $l = 1$ can accommodate six electrons. Further information about the numbers of electrons in subshells can be obtained by examining the photoelectron spectrum of krypton.

ITQ 6   Before proceeding, label the energy levels in Figure 55 (in the answer to ITQ 4) with the values of the second quantum number, l.

If you look at the photoelectron spectrum of krypton (Figure 31) you can obtain further information about the $n = 3$ quantum shell. The atomic number of krypton is 36, and the atom contains electrons in the $n = 1$, $n = 2$, $n = 3$ and $n = 4$ shells.

How can we find out how many electrons are in the $n = 3$ shell? First we need to know how many electrons are in the other shells. We can assume that in any electron shell, the subshell $l = 0$ can contain a maximum of two electrons, and the subshell $l = 1$ can contain a maximum of six electrons. Both of these subshells in the $n = 4$ shell are *full*, a fact that could be deduced from the appearance of another peak (another subshell) in the photoelectron spectrum of the element rubidium, which has one more electron per atom than krypton.

By subtraction we can deduce that the $n = 3$ shell holds 18 electrons, in the following way: two in $n = 1$, eight in $n = 2$, eight in $n = 4$ (total: 18 electrons). So the remaining 18 must be in the $n = 3$ shell.

As well as deducing the total number of electrons in the $n = 3$ shell, you should be able to deduce from the photoelectron spectrum and electron energy-level diagram of krypton (Figures 31 and 55), how many electrons the $l = 2$ subshell can accommodate.

How many is this?

If the $n = 3$ shell contains 18 electrons, including two in the $l = 0$ subshell and six in the $l = 1$ subshell, it follows that the $l = 2$ subshell contains ten electrons ($18 - 2 - 6$).

We now have almost enough information to predict the distribution of electrons in the shells and subshells of any atom. This distribution is called the **electronic configuration** of an element. A few diagrams will make it clear that this facility has been developed by the discussion so far and help us to introduce a shorthand method of writing electronic configuration.

Figure 35 shows the electron energy-level diagrams for several elements, with the electrons (depicted as circles) already inserted in the diagram for sodium.

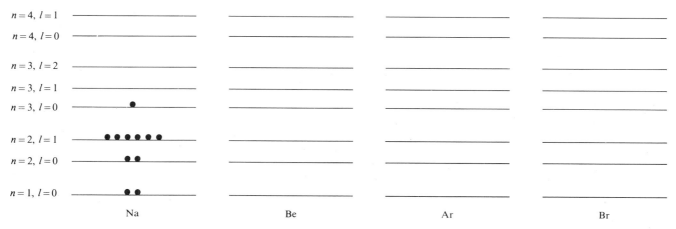

FIGURE 35   Schematic energy-level diagrams for some atoms.

ITQ 7   Complete the diagrams for the other three elements in Figure 35. You will need to know the number of electrons in each of these atoms (see Appendix 1 for atomic numbers.)

Before we proceed to establish and apply the rules for determining the electronic structures of more complicated atoms, it will be convenient to represent the subshells using a shorthand notation instead of drawing diagrams.

6.1 THE s–p–d–f NOTATION

Electronic structures were originally established by the spectroscopic technique that you used in Section 5. In the emission spectrum of sodium the lines appear as several series, one of which consists of *sharp* lines and another of *diffuse* lines. A third series was regarded as the *principal* series, since it is the most intense. The value of the second quantum number is usually denoted by the initial letters of these series, s, p, d and f (f comes from fundamental), so instead of using numbers for particular values of l, we write:

s for subshells with $l = 0$

p for subshells with $l = 1$

d for subshells with $l = 2$

f for subshells with $l = 3$

These letters can be used as a shorthand method of labelling electron energy levels. The lowest energy level in an atom has $n = 1$, $l = 0$. So it is said to be a 1s level. The value of n is denoted by 1, and the value of l is denoted by s.

ITQ 8   Label the levels in Figure 34 using this notation.

The same notation is used to represent the electronic configuration. For example, an atom of helium has two electrons in the 1s level. We say that it has two 1s electrons and we show the number of electrons using a super-script on the s. The electronic configuration of helium is written

$$1s^2$$

and this is spoken as 'one s two'. Similarly, the electronic configurations of other atoms can be written in this shorthand notation.

☐ Taking account of the information in your completed Figure 34, write the electronic configuration of neon using the s–p–d–f notation.

■ The electronic configuration of neon is

$$1s^2 2s^2 2p^6$$

This is simply a statement of the way that the electrons are distributed among the subshells, and these are usually written in order in which the subshells are filled.

SUMMARY OF SECTION 6

1   Information about the electronic structure of atoms that contain many electrons can be obtained by measuring successive ionization energies and from photoelectron spectroscopy.

2   These techniques show that electrons in atoms are contained in shells, and each shell consists of one or more subshells.

3   The shells are numbered from 1 upwards, beginning with the innermost shell, which contains the most tightly bound electrons. These numbers correspond to the principal quantum numbers (n) used to label the energy levels in the hydrogen atom.

4   A shell with principal quantum number n consists of n subshells. These are labelled by a second quantum number, l, which can have values from zero to $(n - 1)$. The values of l are denoted by the letters s, p, d and f, corresponding to $l = 0, 1, 2$ and 3, respectively.

5   Each subshell can accommodate a limited number of electrons: two in an s subshell, six in a p and ten in a d.

6   The labelling of shells and subshells, and the numbers of electrons that they can accommodate, are shown in Table 7.

TABLE 7   Labelling of shells and subshells

Shell	Subshell	Label	Number of electrons
$n = 1$	$l = 0$	s	2
$n = 2$	$l = 0$	s	2
	$l = 1$	p	6
$n = 3$	$l = 0$	s	2
	$l = 1$	p	6
	$l = 2$	d	10

6.2 THE INTERPRETATION OF ATOMIC SPECTRA (AV sequence)

You should now listen to the AV sequence 'The interpretation of atomic spectra', which starts on Tape 2 (Side 2, Band 3) and ends on Tape 3 (Side 1, Band 1). This draws on your knowledge of Sections 5 and 6 and revises many of the ideas introduced there.

1   Emission spectrum of hydrogen

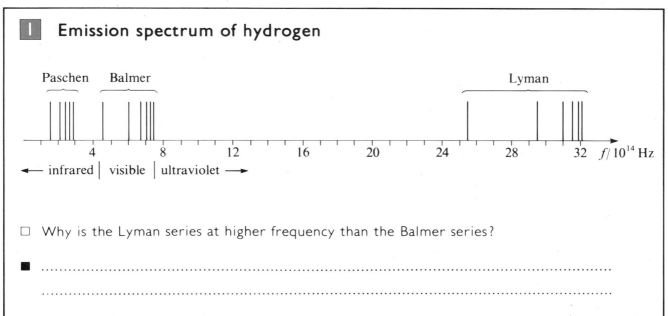

□   Why is the Lyman series at higher frequency than the Balmer series?

■   ....

    ....

2   Energy levels for hydrogen

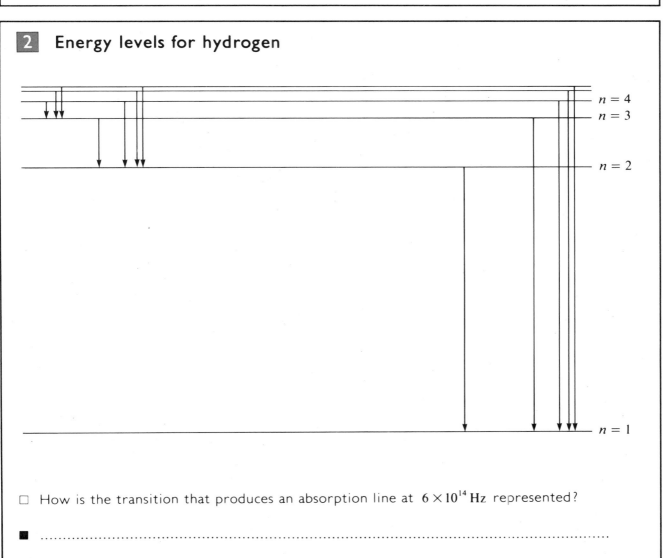

□   How is the transition that produces an absorption line at 6×10^{14} Hz represented?

■   ....

3 Absorption spectrum of hydrogen

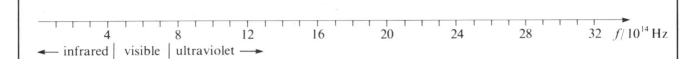

← infrared │ visible │ ultraviolet ⟶

4 Photoelectron spectrum of sodium

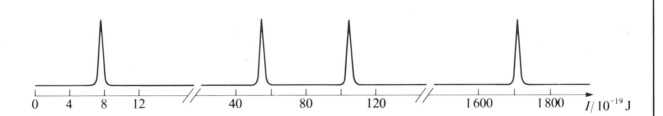

☐ How many energy levels (subshells) are occupied in an atom of sodium?

■ ....

5 Energy-level diagram for sodium

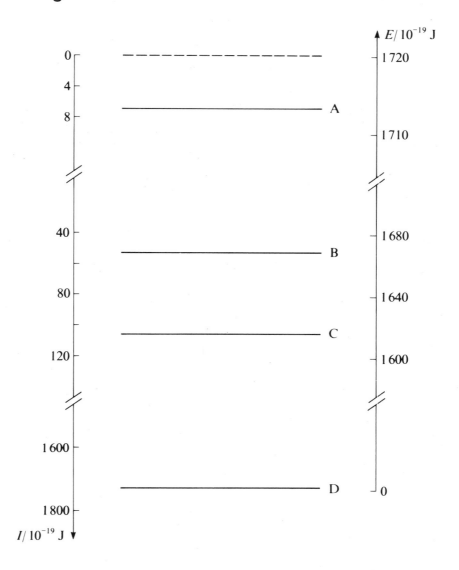

☐ How many electron shells are occupied?

■ ....

☐ What are the labels (1s, etc) for the levels A to D?

Level	n	l	Label
A			
B			
C			
D			

6 Emission spectrum of sodium

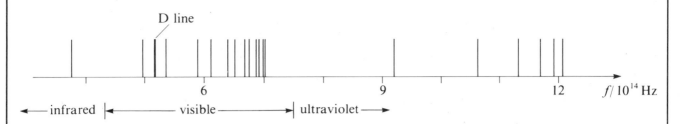

□ How does this spectrum resemble that of hydrogen?

■ ....

....

7 A more simple spectrum of sodium

Energy–frequency relationship: $E = hf$

$$E = 6.626 \times 10^{-34}\,\text{J s} \times f$$

□ What information can we get from the convergence limit of this series?

■ ....

□ In which energy level or subshell is the electron that is involved in each transition in this series?

■ ....

□ What is the energy difference between the levels involved in the transition that produces the D line?

■ ....

8 Energy-level diagram

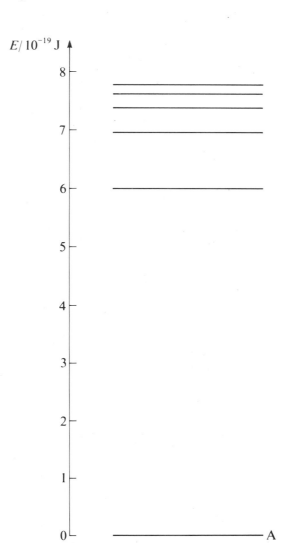

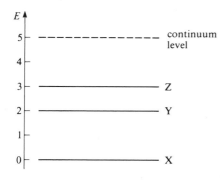

FIGURE 36 The electron energy-level diagram of an atom of the hypothetical element pandemonium. The energy scale is marked in arbitrary energy units.

SAQ 24 Figure 36 shows the electron energy-level diagram of an atom of the hypothetical element pandemonium. In the ground state, only levels X and Y are occupied by electrons and both levels are fully occupied. Use arrows to represent the energy changes corresponding to:

(a) An absorption line in the spectrum;

(b) An emission line in the spectrum;

(c) The ionization energy of an electron in the level Y;

(d) The ejection of a photoelectron produced by a photon of 4 arbitrary energy units.

SAQ 25 Using the information in SAQ 24 and in Figure 36, estimate the lowest ionization energy of the element pandemonium.

SAQ 26 Figure 37 shows the photoelectron spectrum of magnesium. Identify the electron subshells corresponding to each of the ionization energies and decide how many electrons are in each subshell (an atom of magnesium contains 12 electrons). Hence write down the electronic configuration of magnesium.

FIGURE 37 The photoelectron spectrum of magnesium.

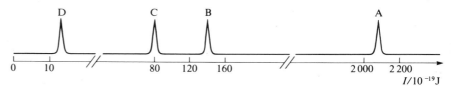

SAQ 27 Figure 38 is the photoelectron spectrum of the gas argon, which exists as single atoms. What evidence is contained in this spectrum for the existence of electron shells and subshells?

FIGURE 38 The photoelectron spectrum of argon.

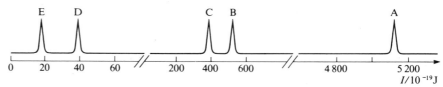

SAQ 28 Using the information in Figure 38, sketch an electron energy-level diagram for argon. Label the levels with values of the principal quantum number and the appropriate letter to denote the second quantum number, using the convention given in Section 6.1.

7 ELECTRON SPIN

In Section 6 we have examined the shell and subshell structure of atoms, and the rules governing electron distribution among the subshells. However, we have not attempted to explain these rules. For example:

Why does the $n = 1$ shell contain two electrons?

Why can different subshells accommodate different maximum numbers of electrons?

These questions can be answered by examining more closely the emission spectra of elements and the way that atoms behave in magnetic fields. We do this in this Section and the next, before developing some general rules for establishing electronic configuration.

Let us first turn our attention to the $n = 1$ shell. Why should this shell be capable of accommodating two, and no more than two, electrons? Here are some experimental clues that can help us answer the question.

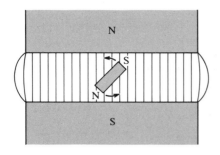

FIGURE 39   A bar magnet in a uniform (homogeneous) magnetic field. The curved arrows indicate the tendency of the bar magnet to align itself parallel to the direction of the homogeneous field. The thin lines show the direction of the magnetic field.

(a)   When a beam of hydrogen atoms is passed through an inhomogeneous (non-uniform) magnetic field, it splits into two beams, both of which are deflected from the straight through path.

(b)   The same experiment performed on a stream of helium atoms produces no splitting or deflection of the beam.

All we can say straight away as a result of this information is that hydrogen atoms have magnetic properties that helium atoms do not have.

How can atoms behave as magnets? Well, you know from Units 5–6 that an electric charge in motion has magnetic properties.

Is there anything in the hydrogen atom that answers this description? Both the electron and the proton are charged. In fact it is the electron that is the source of the magnetic behaviour of the beam of hydrogen atoms. However, helium has twice as many electrons as hydrogen, so it is not immediately obvious why helium atoms should not be deflected in this experiment.

Before we go much further with interpreting the experimental information, it is necessary to consider what effect a *non-uniform* magnetic field has on a bar magnet.

7.1 UNIFORM AND NON-UNIFORM MAGNETIC FIELDS

In Units 5–6 it was explained that a magnetic dipole placed in a uniform magnetic field does not move bodily in a given direction, although it does rotate. You will remember that this is because the north and south poles of the dipole experience equal attraction in the uniform field, the force on one pole being exactly balanced by the force on the other. All that remains is the turning force, which causes the dipole to rotate in order to align itself with the magnetic field (Figure 39). Once it is aligned, it stays put.

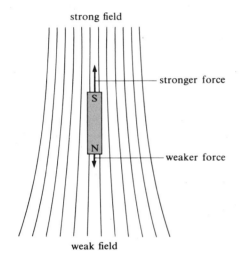

FIGURE 40   In this diagram, the strong field is due to the north pole of another magnet. There is a net force on the magnet in the diagram that tends to move it towards the region in which the magnetic field lines are closest together (i.e. towards the top of the diagram). If the north and south poles of the magnet shown in the diagram were reversed, the magnet would move in the opposite direction, towards the weaker field.

If the magnetic field changes significantly over a distance comparable with the range of observation, it is said to be non-uniform. In this case the forces on opposite poles of the magnet are no longer balanced, one pole experiencing a stronger force than the other, so the magnet will tend to *move* in the direction of the stronger force. Figure 40 illustrates the situation when the field is strongest near the south pole of the magnet, as can be seen from the way the field direction lines crowd together. You will remember from your experiments in Units 5–6 that magnetized objects such as iron filings and paper clips move in this way when subjected to a non-uniform field (for example a bar magnet).

7.2 ELECTRON SPIN AND THE MAGNETIC SPIN QUANTUM NUMBER

In the experiment whose results we presented in observations (a) and (b) above, the geometry of the magnet field is like that in Figure 40. This is produced by a magnet like that shown in Figure 41. One of the pole pieces is a knife-edge, the other a groove, and the magnet pole faces are relatively

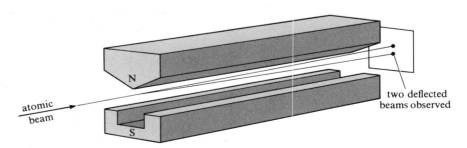

FIGURE 41   The splitting of an atomic beam by a magnetic field.

53

ELECTRON SPIN

PAIRING OF ELECTRONS

UNPAIRED ELECTRONS

MAGNETIC SPIN QUANTUM
NUMBER, m_s

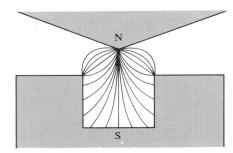

FIGURE 42 The non-uniform field used in the atomic beam experiment.

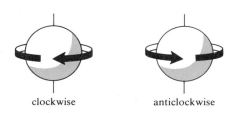

clockwise   anticlockwise

FIGURE 43 The spinning electron.

long. The field strength at the knife-edge is very much higher than at the groove, as shown in Figure 42. Any atomic magnets passing through this very non-uniform field are subject to a deflecting force.

☐ What conclusion can we draw from the information that a beam of hydrogen atoms splits into two under these circumstances?

■ It seems that a random sample of hydrogen atoms behaves as though it contains *two* kinds of magnet, which are deflected differently in the non-uniform field. As one beam is deviated towards the knife-edge, and the other away from it, it appears that the two atomic magnets interact in opposite senses with the applied field.

Let us now consider what motion of the electron could be responsible for the magnetic properties of the hydrogen atom. If we suppose that the electron is orbiting the nucleus, it behaves as a current loop, which has an associated dipole (Units 5–6). However, you know from Figure 13 that the electron distribution in the hydrogen atom is spherical, so all directions of alignment of the dipole are equally probable. Therefore, there is no orbital magnetism associated with the electron in a spherical orbital. So the hydrogen atom in its ground state has no orbital magnetism.

If the magnetism does not result from orbiting motion of the electron, it must be the consequence of some other type of motion of the electron. There seems to be some kind of circulation of the charge carried by the electron. We can think of this as **spin**: rotation of the electron about its own axis. This rotation is, in effect, a loop of electric current, which produces a magnetic field.

The splitting of the beam in two directions indicates that there are just two ways the electron can spin; we can think of these as being clockwise and anticlockwise (Figure 43). The magnetic field produced by an electron spinning clockwise will have opposite polarity to that produced by an electron spinning anticlockwise, because it corresponds to an electric current in the opposite direction.

☐ Now suggest what the two beams observed in experiment (a) for hydrogen atoms might correspond to.

■ Using the model of an electron in Figure 43, we can interpret the experiment. One beam is due to atoms with clockwise-spinning electrons, and the other to atoms with anticlockwise-spinning electrons.

There is an equal probability that the single electron in any hydrogen atom has either kind of spin. In the absence of a magnetic field, the energy of the electron is independent of the direction of its spin. Only the application of the field reveals the existence of the different 'states of spinning'. As Figure 44 shows, the electron spinning anticlockwise has a slightly different energy in the field from the one spinning clockwise.

☐ What conclusion can you now draw from the observation that helium atoms are undeflected by the non-uniform field?

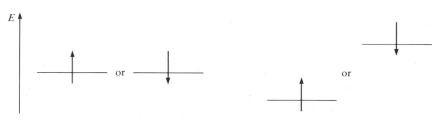

(a) no magnetic field   (b) in the magnetic field

FIGURE 44 The effect of a magnetic field on the spinning electron of the hydrogen atom. The upward- and downward-pointing arrows indicate the clockwise and anticlockwise spin of the electron, respectively.

■ A helium atom has *two* electrons in the 1s level. The absence of magnetism can only be explained by assuming that the two electron 'magnets' have opposite polarity, so that they cancel each other out. In other words, the two electrons in the $n = 1$ shell must have opposite spins. We say that the spins are **paired**.

When we study the magnetic behaviour of other atoms with filled subshells, we discover that they have no magnetic properties. This means that all electron spins must be paired when a shell or subshell is full. When a subshell is partly filled we generally observe the magnetic effects of unpaired electron spins.

The spin of an electron can be indicated by another quantum number, called the **magnetic spin quantum number**, m_s, which is assigned the values $+\frac{1}{2}$ or $-\frac{1}{2}$.

We have now gone some way to answer one of the questions asked at the start of this section, namely why are there just two electrons in the $n = 1$ shell? We now know that this shell consists of *one* subshell, which can accommodate only two electrons with opposite spin. In the helium atom, where the $n = 1$ shell is full, with *two* electrons, the photoelectron spectrum shows that there is just one energy level corresponding to this one subshell. In the hydrogen atom, which contains only one electron, the spin is **unpaired**.

SUMMARY OF SECTION 7

1   A beam of hydrogen atoms is split into two deflected beams by a non-uniform magnetic field. This observation indicates that the atom behaves as a magnet, a suggestion which is explained by assuming that the electron in the atom spins in one of two directions, clockwise or anticlockwise.

2   The magnetic spin quantum number, m_s, is introduced to describe the electron spin (as $m_s = +\frac{1}{2}$ or $m_s = -\frac{1}{2}$), and to explain why the $n = 1$ shell can accommodate just two electrons.

SAQ 29   What would you expect the effect of a non-uniform magnetic field to be on a beam of atoms of (i) Ne, (ii), Na, (iii) Kr?

8 DEGENERACY AND SUBSHELLS

At the beginning of Section 7 we raised two questions. The first of these, concerning the reason why the $n = 1$ shell can accommodate two electrons, has been answered in Section 7.

The question that we now have to consider is slightly more complex. Why should a p subshell be able to accommodate six electrons? Does this mean that there is one orbital that can accommodate six electrons? Or does it mean that the p subshell consists of several orbitals? Remember that 'orbital' is the name given to the distribution of an electron in an atom.

The evidence from photoelectron spectroscopy is that just *one* peak is observed corresponding to ionization from a p subshell, which shows that under normal conditions all six electrons in the p subshell have the same energy. You saw in Section 7.2 that a non-uniform magnetic field can alter the energy of an electron in the atom. It would be interesting to see if the six electrons still have identical energies when such a magnetic field is applied.

One way to investigate the effect of a magnetic field on p electron energies is to look at the behaviour in a magnetic field of the transition of an electron from a p subshell (a p to s transition) in the emission spectrum of a suitable atom. It is best to avoid complicating effects due to electron spin, so we choose an atom where the highest occupied level in the ground state is an s level that contains two paired electrons, a full s level.

The atom we have chosen is magnesium, which has a full 3s subshell and in which the lowest unoccupied level is a p level. You will remember that its ground-state configuration is $1s^2 2s^2 2p^6 3s^2$ (SAQ 26). An intense line at 1.05×10^{15} Hz (in the ultraviolet) has been identified as corresponding to a transition from an excited state, where an electron is in the 3p subshell, to the ground state.

When the emission spectrum of magnesium is obtained in a very strong magnetic field (stronger by a factor of about 1 000 than anything the magnets in your Experiment Kit can produce) a tiny splitting of the line *is* observed. Under careful examination the line at 1.05×10^{15} Hz is seen to consist of three closely spaced lines.

☐ What do you infer from the appearance of three lines in place of one?

■ The p subshell (occupied in the excited state), which consisted of just one electron energy level in the absence of a magnetic field, must consist of *three* levels in a magnetic field.

This very significant result, first observed by Peiter Zeeman in 1896, is called the **Zeeman effect**. It shows that the p subshell is actually made up of *three levels*, which have identical energies in the absence of a magnetic field. We describe *two* or more electron energy levels that have the same energy as **degenerate** levels. As Figure 45 shows, these degenerate levels are differentiated only in the presence of a magnetic field. The three p levels can each accommodate two electrons.

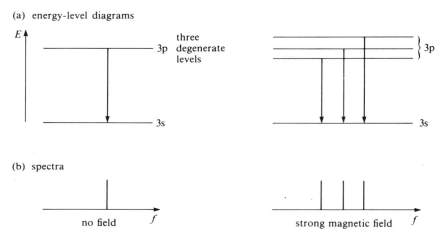

FIGURE 45   Splitting of the p to s transition for magnesium in a strong magnetic field.

In Section 3.1 we introduced the idea that an electron in an atom is orbiting the nucleus, although not in a circular or elliptical path, but in a region of space depicted by Figure 13. The electron is said to be contained in an orbital. Each of the degenerate levels that are present in an atom, e.g. the three degenerate p levels, corresponds to a different orbital. Therefore there are three degenerate p orbitals for each principal quantum number.

It now begins to look as though the maximum number of electrons that an orbital can accommodate is two. If a subshell holds more than two electrons, this is because the subshell consists of several degenerate orbitals. These degenerate orbitals can be differentiated only in a magnetic field.

At this point we have a confession to make. In presenting evidence about interaction of electron magnets with applied magnetic fields, we have deliberately chosen the very simplest cases. For example, we were careful to avoid discussion of the effect of a magnetic field on the p to s transition in an atom like sodium (ground-state configuration $1s^2 2s^2 2p^6 3s^1$), where the atom has a magnetic effect due to spin of the unpaired electron. Magnetism due to electron *spin* can interact with that due to electron *orbital motion* to produce highly complex splitting patterns for some atoms in a magnetic field. We have chosen examples where magnetic effects are due to *either* spin *or* orbital motion but not a combination of both.

SAQ 30   What effect would you expect application of a magnetic field to have on the spectral line from the $2s^1$ to $1s^1$ transition in hydrogen, if the transition were observable?

SAQ 31   What effect would you expect application of a strong magnetic field to have on the transition of a helium atom from the electronic configuration $1s^1 2s^1$ to the electronic configuration $1s^2$? (You may assume that the electrons in the helium atom with electronic configuration $1s^1 2s^1$ have opposite spins, as in the ground state configuration $1s^2$. Therefore there is no net magnetic effect due to electron spin in the excited state.)

SAQ 32   If a stream of beryllium atoms were passed through an inhomogeneous magnetic field, what effect would you expect to see?

8.1 THE MAGNETIC QUANTUM NUMBER

We now need to introduce yet another quantum number to distinguish the individual degenerate levels or orbitals within each subshell.

You will remember from Section 6 the values that the second quantum number has for s, p and d subshells. From the Zeeman effect you have seen that a p subshell, which can accommodate six electrons, has three degenerate orbitals. A d subshell, which can accommodate ten electrons, has five degenerate orbitals. We can summarize these properties as follows:

Subshell	Second quantum number	Number of degenerate orbitals
s	$l = 0$	one
p	$l = 1$	three
d	$l = 2$	five

You probably begin to see a pattern here. The number of degenerate orbitals is $2l + 1$ in all cases.

The quantum number that we use to label the degenerate orbitals that make up p or d subshells is called the **magnetic quantum number** and is given the symbol m_l. We choose the quantum numbers so that they span the integers between $+l$ and $-l$. Thus, the three orbitals in the p subshell ($l = 1$) are numbered $m_l = +1$, $m_l = 0$, $m_l = -1$.

☐   What magnetic quantum numbers identify the following:

   (i)   the one orbital in the s subshell,

   (ii)   the five orbitals in the d subshell?

■   (i) The s subshell has $m_l = 0$; (ii) the d subshell has $m_l = +2$, $m_l = +1$, $m_l = 0$, $m_l = -1$, and $m_l = -2$.

We do not propose at this stage to go into the reason why p orbitals are affected by a magnetic field. We can merely indicate that it is connected with the fact that the p and d orbitals, unlike the s orbital in Figure 13, are *not* spherically symmetric.

SAQ 33   The subshell with $l = 3$ is called an f subshell. How many degenerate orbitals would you expect it to contain?

8.2 FOUR QUANTUM NUMBERS

We can now describe each electron in a p sub-shell completely by means of four quantum numbers. No electron in an atom can have the same set of values for the four quantum numbers as any other electron in the atom.

THE FOUR QUANTUM NUMBERS

The principal quantum number, n	$n = 1, 2, 3 \ldots$
The second quantum number, l	$l = 0, 1, 2 \ldots (n-1)$
The magnetic quantum number, m_l	$m_l = -l \ldots 0 \ldots +l$
The magnetic spin quantum number, m_s	$m_s = \pm \frac{1}{2}$

ITQ 9 Describe all six 2p electrons by listing their quantum numbers.

You will see in Section 9 how this procedure can be applied to describe the electronic configuration of any atom.

SUMMARY OF SECTION 8

1 A p subshell can accommodate six electrons because the subshell consists of three orbitals of equal energy (degenerate), each capable of holding two electrons.

2 Evidence for this degeneracy is found when atomic spectra are produced in a strong magnetic field; in the magnetic field the degenerate levels are separated into levels of different energy. The degenerate levels are labelled with the magnetic quantum number m_l, which has values from $-l$ to $+l$.

3 Each electron in an atom can therefore be labelled by four quantum numbers, n, l, m_l and m_s, which distinguish it from all other electrons in the atom.

SAQ 34 How many electrons do you now expect the $n = 3$ shell to be capable of accommodating? What is the electronic configuration of the $n = 3$ shell?

9 ELECTRONIC CONFIGURATIONS OF THE ELEMENTS

We are now in a position to draw together the ideas that we have developed about electron energy levels and quantum numbers in order to establish the electronic configurations of the elements. If you are wondering why we have spent so much time on this aspect of atomic structure, remember what we said at the start of this discussion: not only is our knowledge of atomic structure a fascinating result of human curiosity, but the chemistry of the elements is very dependent on their electronic structures. A knowledge of electronic structure is often a useful aid to remembering, understanding and sometimes to predicting the chemical behaviour of elements.

At this stage you should be able to write the electronic structure of the atom of any element up to atomic number 18, argon, using the appropriate sequence of electron subshells (1s, 2s, 2p, 3s, 3p) and remembering the degeneracy of the levels. To do this you follow the rules 1 to 6 set out in the box.

RULES FOR WRITING ELECTRONIC CONFIGURATIONS

1 In the ground state the electrons fill the innermost (lowest energy) shells first.

2 The electron shells are labelled in sequence by the principal quantum number, n, which can have values 1, 2, 3, etc.

3 The electron shells designated by the principal quantum number are divided into subshells, designated by the second quantum number, l.

4 The *number* of subshells in a shell is equal to the *value* of the principal quantum number (because l has values 0, 1, 2, ... up to $(n - 1)$).

5 Within an electron shell, the energies of the subshells increase with the value of the second quantum number, l.

6 There is a maximum number of electrons that any subshell can hold:

$l = 0$, s: two electrons

$l = 1$, p: six electrons

$l = 2$, d: ten electrons

ITQ 10 Write the electronic configurations for the elements oxygen and sulphur. The atomic numbers are 8 and 16, respectively.

□ Now write the electronic configuration for manganese (atomic number 25).

■ If you have followed the rules, you have probably written:

$1s^2 2s^2 2p^6 3s^2 3p^6 3d^7$

If you wrote this, you have correctly applied the procedure for filling the subshells with electrons, but you have probably assumed, quite reasonably, that the 3d subshell fills before the 4s subshell. In fact this assumption is *wrong*. As you know from the electron energy-level diagram for hydrogen (Figure 19) or for any other atom, the energies of the *electron shells* converge as n increases. Also, as you can see from the photoelectron spectra of Ne, Ar and Kr (Figures 31 and 38), the separations in energy of the s, p and d *subshells* within any shell increase as the elements get heavier. A consequence of this is that the 4s subshell is actually filled before the 3d. The correct electronic configuration for manganese is:

Mn $1s^2 2s^2 2p^6 3s^2 3p^6 4s^2 3d^5$

and the electron energy-level diagram is as shown in Figure 46. Note that because the 4s subshell is filled before the 3d, the electronic configuration is written in the order shown. Notice too that, although the 4s subshell is filled before the 3d, for heavier elements such as krypton, the *full* 3d subshell lies at a lower energy than the full 4s subshell, as Figure 55 implies.

In representing the electronic configuration of an element in the way shown above for manganese, you indicate how the electrons occupy the energy levels. The configuration also indicates the first two quantum numbers, n and l, of each of the electrons in the atom. The electronic structure of an atom can be represented in a slightly different and more informative way in which the spin and magnetic quantum numbers are also depicted. This is done by representing each orbital as a box, and by representing the electron as an arrow pointing up or down to indicate its spin, as we did in Figure 44.

To take one of the simplest cases, helium, the 1s orbital is represented by a single box, and two half-headed arrows represent the electrons:

He
1s

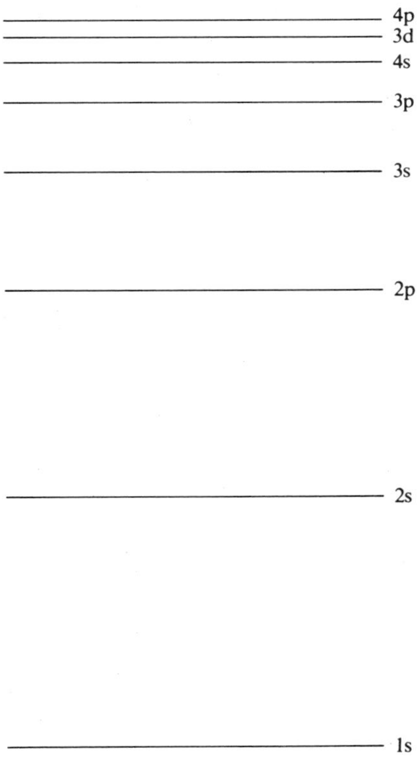

4p
3d
4s

3p

3s

2p

2s

1s

FIGURE 46 The electron energy-level diagram up to subshell 4p.

Notice that this form of representation vividly shows the pairing of the electrons in the 1s orbital of helium. To give you another example of this box system of showing electronic configuration, the magnesium atom, which has the electronic structure $1s^2 2s^2 2p^6 3s^2$, is represented as:

Mg $\boxed{\uparrow\downarrow}$ $\boxed{\uparrow\downarrow}$ $\boxed{\uparrow\downarrow}\boxed{\uparrow\downarrow}\boxed{\uparrow\downarrow}$ $\boxed{\uparrow\downarrow}$
    1s   2s   2p   3s

Notice that within each orbital the electron spins are paired.

9.1 HUND'S RULE

Note that we have single boxes for 1s and 2s, since they each contain only one pair of electrons, and a triple box for 2p because the 2p subshell is triply degenerate.

☐ Use this system to show the electronic structure of argon (atomic number 18).

■ The electronic structure of argon is $1s^2 2s^2 2p^6 3s^2 3p^6$, and so it can be depicted as:

Ar $\boxed{\uparrow\downarrow}$ $\boxed{\uparrow\downarrow}$ $\boxed{\uparrow\downarrow}\boxed{\uparrow\downarrow}\boxed{\uparrow\downarrow}$ $\boxed{\uparrow\downarrow}$ $\boxed{\uparrow\downarrow}\boxed{\uparrow\downarrow}\boxed{\uparrow\downarrow}$
    1s   2s   2p   3s   3p

A d subshell can accommodate ten electrons, that is five pairs, and is represented by a five-compartment box.

Now try to write out the electronic configuration of sulphur, using the box system. Its atomic number is 16. The order of filling the subshells is 1s, 2s, 2p, 3s, 3p, and the electronic structure is $1s^2 2s^2 2p^6 3s^2 3p^4$. Here are the boxes labelled up to 3p:

S $\boxed{}$ $\boxed{}$ $\boxed{}\boxed{}\boxed{}$ $\boxed{}$ $\boxed{}\boxed{}\boxed{}$
   1s   2s   2p   3s   3p

You should have been faced with a dilemma when you attempted to put the arrows in your 3p boxes. Is there any way of deciding whether to write

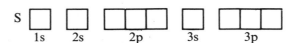

$\boxed{\uparrow\downarrow}\boxed{\uparrow}\boxed{\uparrow}$ or $\boxed{\uparrow\downarrow}\boxed{\uparrow\downarrow}\boxed{}$?
        3p   3p

That is, should the electrons be *paired*, as on the right, or be left *unpaired* if possible, as on the left?

The results of experimental determinations of electronic configurations by spectroscopy show that this question can be answered by an empirical rule known as **Hund's rule**:

> Within any subshell, there will be the maximum number of *unpaired* electrons in an atom in its ground state.

The left-hand version is correct in this case, because it shows two unpaired electrons whereas there are none in the right-hand version.

Now, with this rule, you should be able to write the electronic structure of the atoms of any element, given the correct sequence of subshells. Figure 47 shows the order in which all the subshells are filled: you merely follow the snake.

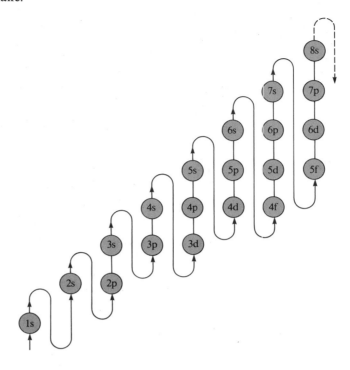

FIGURE 47   The order in which the subshells are filled.

Show the electronic structure of ground-state atoms of phosphorus (15), zinc (30) and cobalt (27), using both the s–p–d–f notation and the box method (atomic numbers are shown in brackets.) Use the sequence of subshells in Figure 47. Remember to fill the subshells of lowest energy first, irrespective of quantum number.

The structures are:

P $1s^2 2s^2 2p^6 3s^2 3p^3$

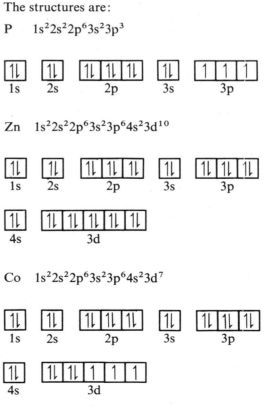

Zn $1s^2 2s^2 2p^6 3s^2 3p^6 4s^2 3d^{10}$

Co $1s^2 2s^2 2p^6 3s^2 3p^6 4s^2 3d^7$

Now try chromium (atomic number 24).

No doubt you predicted the configuration $1s^2 2s^2 2p^6 3s^2 3p^6 4s^2 3d^4$. If so, you have correctly interpreted the rules. However, a few elements do not obey the rules precisely. In atoms with many electrons, the energies of the outer subshells are sometimes very close together indeed, as you can see from Figure 46, and occasionally the presence of electrons in, say, the 3d subshell changes the relative energy of the 4s subshell, so that sometimes it contains two electrons and sometimes only one. We know this from experiments.

Can you guess what type of experiment?

This sort of information is obtained from a detailed examination of the atomic spectra of elements, which shows the electronic configuration of chromium to be:

Cr $1s^2 2s^2 2p^6 3s^2 3p^6 4s^1 3d^5$

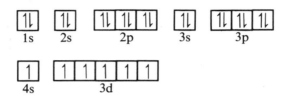

Clearly, from the anomalous electronic configuration of chromium, the energies of the configurations

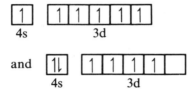

must be very similar. *Knowing* the answer, it is possible to look for sensible reasons for it, but to predict it would be much more difficult.

SUMMARY OF SECTION 9

Here is a summary of the procedures and rules you would use to write electronic structures, given the order of filling subshells (Figure 47). A list of electronic configurations of all the elements is given in Appendix 2.

1   The atomic number of the element tells you the number of electrons in a neutral atom.

2   These electrons are 'fed' into the electron subshells using the following rules:

   (a)   The electrons fill the subshells of lowest energy first (Figure 47).

   (b)   Within any subshell, the number of electrons with unpaired spins is a maximum (Hund's rule).

3   The number of possible values of the quantum numbers is determined by the rules:

$$n = 1, 2, 3, \text{etc.}$$
$$l = 0 \text{ to } n - 1$$
$$m_l = -l \text{ to } +l$$
$$m_s = \tfrac{1}{2} \text{ or } -\tfrac{1}{2}$$

You probably no longer need apply rule 3 in this way; you probably just remember that:

an s subshell can accommodate two electrons (one pair, with opposite spins);

a p subshell can accommodate six electrons (three pairs);

a d subshell can accommodate ten electrons (five pairs);

an f subshell can accommodate fourteen electrons (seven pairs);

within any atom, no two electrons can have the same set of four quantum numbers.

We can now summarize the information we have about the maximum number of electrons that can be accommodated in various subshells in the following way:

Electron Shells

with principal quantum numbers $n = 1$ 2   3   4

            can accommodate   2   8   18   32   electrons

Electron Subshells

denoted by values of $l = 0$ 1   2   3

     are represented by   s   p   d   f

and can accommodate   2   6   10   14 electrons

This means that a filled $n = 4$ electron shell consists of filled subshells represented by

$$4s^2 4p^6 4d^{10} 4f^{14}$$

SAQ 35 Write the electronic configuration of nitrogen using the box representation.

SAQ 36 Using the sequence of subshells given in Figure 47 write the electronic configuration of copper ($Z = 29$) in the s–p–d–f notation.

If you are interested in trying more examples of this kind of question, there is a computer-assisted learning program (CALCHEM) available at a terminal at Study Centres or Summer School, which gives revision exercises in electronic configurations.

10 FIRST IONIZATION ENERGIES

We have said at various stages that our interest in the electronic structures of atoms arises mainly because electronic structure determines to a large extent the chemical properties of the elements. This dependence of chemistry on electronic structure is hardly surprising. As atoms approach each other to react it is the electrons that first interact or exchange; the diameter of an atom (the region containing the electrons) is about 10 000 times the nuclear diameter.

Also, as you saw at the start of Section 6 (Figure 27), the energies needed to remove the first one or two electrons from an atom are much less than those needed to remove subsequent electrons. Not surprisingly, therefore, the energy required to remove the *first* electron from an atom of each element is for chemists an interesting quantity. One of the most valuable and chemically revealing sets of data that emerges from the study of electronic structure is the way that **first ionization energies**, I_1, vary from element to element. Let us examine this variation.

TABLE 8 The first ionization energies for the elements up to calcium

Atomic number	$I_1/10^{-19}$ J
1 (H)	21.78
2 (He)	39.22
3 (Li)	8.63
4 (Be)	14.93
5 (B)	13.29
6 (C)	18.03
7 (N)	23.28
8 (O)	21.85
9 (F)	27.90
10 (Ne)	34.54
11 (Na)	8.23
12 (Mg)	12.25
13 (Al)	9.59
14 (Si)	13.05
15 (P)	16.80
16 (S)	16.59
17 (Cl)	20.84
18 (Ar)	25.24
19 (K)	6.95
20 (Ca)	9.79

Table 8 lists the first ionization energies for the elements up to atomic number 20 (calcium).

> Plot the first ionization energies against atomic number in Figure 48 (the first three points are given). What is the major feature of the Figure?

In looking at the values in Table 8 or at the points on your plot, you are comparing the elements in order of increasing atomic number. From one element to the next an extra proton is added to the nucleus and an extra electron is added to the atom. The Table and plot compare the energies required to remove the *least* tightly bound electron from atoms of different elements. It seems likely that the last electron added in proceeding from one atom to another is the least tightly bound electron.

The most striking feature of your plot in Figure 48 is the way in which the ionization energies are arranged in ascending groups.

☐ How many elements are there in each of the ascending groups which end at the three major peaks in the Figure?

■ These numbers are 2 (up to He), 8 (up to Ne) and 8 (up to Ar).

☐ Is this reminiscent of any other data that you have encountered in the study of atomic structure?

■ If you compare the pattern of first ionization energies in Figure 48 with the ionization energies of individual electrons in the *same* atom, for example argon in ITQ 7, you will notice the same grouping of electrons 2, 8, 8. The reasons for these numbers should now be familiar from the discussion of quantum numbers and occupation of energy levels by electrons (Sections 5–9).

We can, of course, extend our discussion of first ionization energies beyond calcium. Figure 49 shows a plot up to radon.

☐ Do any of the features that you noticed up to atomic number 20 continue beyond there? List them.

■ The major peaks continue and each is immediately followed by a point in a minimum position. You probably also noticed similarities in the arrangements of the points leading up to each maximum.

You may also have noticed a similarity that underlies much of the emphasis we have placed on our study of electronic configuration. In Section 6 the elements we chose to study by photoelectron spectroscopy were precisely those that occur as single atoms: He, Ne, Ar, Kr and Xe. Notice their position at the peaks in the plot of first ionization energies (Figure 49). Their existence as single atoms (monatomic gases) results from their reluctance to combine chemically with other elements or themselves. This is turn suggests some connection between electronic configuration and chemical behaviour. Helium has a full subshell ($1s^2$). Each of the other atoms in this group has an outer shell with the configuration s^2p^6 (two full subshells), which appears to render these elements especially inert to reaction.

Unlike He, Ne, etc., the elements at the troughs of Figure 49 (Li, Na, K, Rb, Cs) are all particularly reactive. If this is related to their low ionization energies—their willingness to lose the single s electron in their outer shell—the connection between electronic configuration and chemical behaviour seems to strengthen.

To take another example, the chemical properties of the elements immediately to the left of the peaks in Figure 49 (F, Cl, Br, I) show similarities. These elements combine with the elements Li, Na, etc., for example, to produce crystalline substances such as common salt.

The intricate and fascinating relationship between electronic structure and chemical behaviour is a topic we shall examine more closely in Units 13–14.

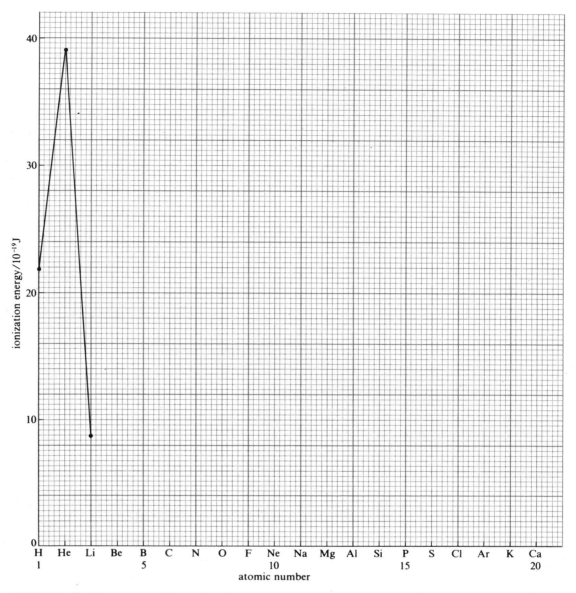

FIGURE 48   Your graph of first ionization energy versus atomic number for the elements up to calcium.

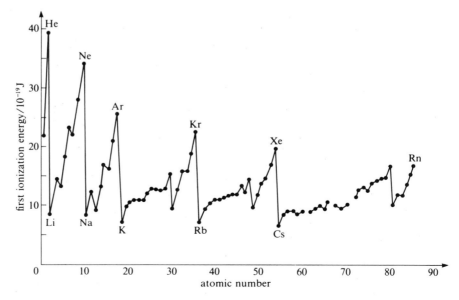

FIGURE 49   Graph of ionization energy versus atomic number for the first 86 elements.

SUMMARY OF SECTION 10

1   A plot of first ionization energy versus atomic number reveals a pattern that suggests that elements can be arranged in groups according to the values of their ionization energy.

2   The pattern of first ionization energies reflects the electronic configurations of the elements: full subshells correspond to relatively high first ionization energies.

3   A comparison of the reactivity of elements with position on the ionization energy plot suggests a connection between chemical properties and electronic structure.

SAQ 37   On the basis of the evidence in Figure 49, how many electron shells are occupied (not necessarily fully) in xenon?

SAQ 38   According to the information in Figure 49, which of the gases He, Ne, Ar, Kr, and Xe has the most easily removed outer electron?

11 TV NOTES: ELECTRONS AND ATOMS

In 1897 Professor J. J. Thomson reported the results of some experiments from which he concluded that atoms of all substances contain common sub-atomic particles. The particle that Thomson discovered was the electron. This programme deals with some of the experiments that led to the conclusion that electrons are small negatively charged particles. You will also see experiments in which the charge and mass of an electron can be measured and how these experiments can be adapted to measure the masses of atoms.

In the experiment in which the charge of the electron is determined, the electric charge on small drops of oil is measured. Note that these oil-drops have *lost* electrons, so that they are *positively* charged. To vary the charge on these drops, the drops are bombarded with β-radiation, which is just a stream of electrons. As a drop picks up electrons, the positive charge that the drop initially carries is reduced.

If you have read Sections 1–3, you will have a better appreciation of the importance of the experiments, but it is not essential to have read any of the text before watching this programme.

The passage of electricity along a metal wire is a flow of electrons. To study the electrons, we have to get them out of the metal, preferably in a vessel from which the air has been removed—into a vacuum. This is achieved by heating a wire filament. To produce a beam of electrons, the electrons are accelerated by a potential difference between the filament (negative) and a metal plate (positive) in which is cut an appropriate hole: a small round hole produces a narrow beam, a slit produces a ribbon beam.

A broad beam of electrons is observed to cast a sharp shadow of a cross (Figure 50), showing that electrons travel in straight lines. A narrow beam of electrons is deflected from its path by the potential difference between two plates above and below the beam (Figure 51). The deflection of the electron beam away from the negative plate and towards the positive plate is proof that electrons are negatively charged.

The charge of an individual particle (one electron) was first measured by Robert Millikan in 1909. The results of Millikan's experiment also demonstrate that the charge of each electron is the same. You can now prove this for yourself, using the results obtained in the programme, together with the results obtained later. These are given in Table 9.

In the Millikan experiment, oil-drops are sprayed between two metal plates. Friction between the drops and the air results in the transfer of electrons between drops and molecules in the air, leaving the drops with a positive

FIGURE 50   The shadow of a cross cast by a beam of electrons.

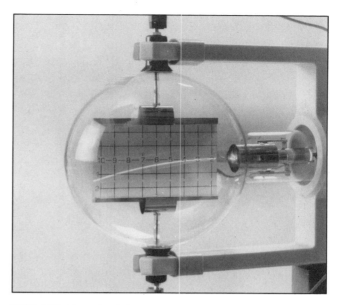

FIGURE 51   The deflection of a beam of electrons by the potential difference between two plates.

TABLE 9   Results of the Millikan experiment

Reading	V/volts	$\dfrac{2V_4}{V}$	$\dfrac{3V_4}{V}$	$\dfrac{4V_4}{V}$	n
1	263				
2	520				
3	700				
4	1055				

charge. One such electrically charged oil-drop is held poised between two charged metal plates. Throughout the experiment the same drop is used. Thus, the downward, gravitational force on the drop is constant. The upward force is determined by the charge on the drop, the distance d between the plates and the electrical potential difference V between the plates. If the charge on the oil-drop arises because it has lost a number n of electrons, each with charge e, its charge is positive and equal to $+ne$. The upward force on the drop is then

$$\text{force up} = \frac{neV}{d} = \text{constant for a particular drop} \qquad (11)$$

Now remember that even if n, the number of electrons lost, is changed, the force down remains constant. (This is the gravitational force on the drop.)

☐ Which other quantity was varied to ensure that the upward force equalled the downward force?
■ You saw the voltage V being adjusted.

In what way is n related to V according to Equation 11?

If the electronic charge e is constant, and since the apparatus is of fixed size (d constant), then e and d can be included in the constant in Equation 11. This gives

$$nV = \text{constant} \qquad (12)$$

where the constant is now different from the one in Equation 11.

In Table 9, which of the readings corresponds to the *lowest* charge on the drop?

Equation 12 indicates that the smaller the charge on the drop, the greater must be the potential difference between the plates, in order that nV will remain constant. Hence, the reading with the *highest* value of V corresponds to the *lowest* charge, reading 4. So concentrate on this reading and on the next highest value of V, reading 3. For these two readings we can write

$$n_3 V_3 = n_4 V_4$$

In this equation both n_3 and n_4 are unknown, but both must be whole numbers if the charge on all electrons really is the same. To find integral values of n_3 and n_4, try setting n_4 equal to 1, then 2 and so on. For example if $n_4 = 1$,

$$n_3 = \frac{1 \times 1\,055}{700} = 1.507$$

Obviously, n_4 does not equal 1 because this value of n_3 is not a whole number. Now try setting n_4 equal to other whole numbers. If the assumptions about the electron are correct, you should find a value that gives an integer for n_3 and also for n_1 and n_2; that is, you should find a column in Table 9 in which each ratio is equal to a whole number. But remember that all experiments involve some uncertainty, so you can expect a few per cent deviation from whole numbers.

When you have found a value of n_4 which satisfies your expectation, you can complete the last column in Table 9.

Millikan was able to go a stage further than this and actually measure the charge of the electron. It has the approximate value 1.602×10^{-19} coulomb.

You also saw that a beam of electrons is deflected by the magnetic field produced in the region between two coils of wire through which an electric current passes (Figure 52). This deflection depends on the *charge* of the particle and on the *mass* of the particle. So from this kind of experiment it is possible to determine the ratio, $e : m_e$, of the charge to the mass of the electron. This ratio was first measured in 1897 by Thomson, but to do it, he also needed to know the velocity of the electrons in the beam. He was able to determine the velocity from measurements of the electric potential difference and the magnetic field when the two forces, electric and magnetic, exactly balance: when the electron beam has a linear path as in Figure 53. The value he obtained was of the order of $10^{11}\,\mathrm{C\,kg^{-1}}$. Modern estimates give the value as:

$$e : m_e \approx 1.8 \times 10^{11}\,\mathrm{C\,kg^{-1}}$$

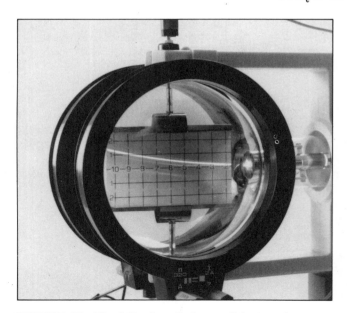

FIGURE 52   The deflection of a beam of electrons by a magnetic field.

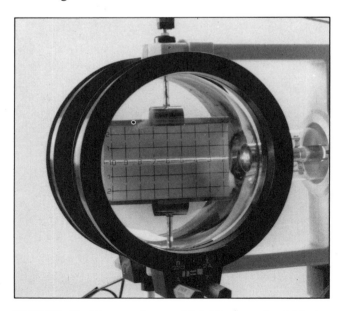

FIGURE 53   The experiment of J. J. Thomson, in which the electric and magnetic forces are balanced in order to determine the velocity of the electron beam and hence the ratio $e : m_e$ for the electron.

ITQ 11 What is the mass of the electron as deduced from these values of e and $e : m_e$?

ITQ 12 What is the ratio of the mass of a hydrogen atom (m_H) to the mass of an electron? ($m_H = 1.67 \times 10^{-27}$ kg.)

Thomson also observed that *positive* rays are produced when an electric current passes through a tube from which most of the air has been removed; these rays can be studied if a hole is made in the negatively charged electrode. The programme showed how, with an experiment similar to his determination of $e : m_e$ for the electron, Thomson was able to measure the masses of the positively charged particles of 'positive rays'. These are ionic particles—charged atoms. In a modern version of this apparatus, the ions in the ion beam are separated when they follow a curved path in a magnetic field. The magnetic field provided by the large magnet acts on the ions in a similar fashion to the way that the small magnet acts on the steel balls in the model you saw. Ions of smaller mass follow a tighter curve than heavier ions. To detect each of the ions in turn, the strength of the field can be varied so that ions of different mass (or strictly charge: mass ratio) arrive successively at the ion collector.

The result is a plot that is strictly of ion current against field strength. But this is effectively a plot of the number of ions against the mass of the ions. In terms of the model it represents the number of steel balls of a particular mass plotted against the mass of the balls. We call a plot of this kind a mass spectrum.

The mass spectrum of neon was shown to consist of three peaks, proving that neon contains atoms of three different masses, ^{20}Ne, ^{21}Ne and ^{22}Ne. Atoms of an element that have different masses are called isotopes.

12 TV NOTES: STEEL, STARS AND SPECTRA

This programme deals with a subject that has enormous theoretical and practical implications, atomic spectroscopy. You may have already observed some spectra with your spectroscope. As part of the physics Summer School experiment you will study atomic spectra with a more sophisticated instrument. You should then find it helpful to have watched this programme. Through the spectra of atoms we learn about their internal structure, a knowledge that forms the basis of our understanding of the chemical behaviour of elements and how they combine. Atomic spectroscopy happens also to be among the most widely used techniques for the analysis of substances.

When you watch the programme, pay special attention to the changes that take place in atoms when they absorb and emit light. This will help you to understand how atomic spectra and atomic structure are related.

The programme began with the problem of analysing a sample of steel at a steel smelter. The steel, which arrives as scrap metal—often scrapped cars—is first melted. As a liquid it is uniform: it has the same composition (or distribution of elements) throughout. This composition has to conform to the specification of the customer, in this case a car manufacturer. For some elements, such as carbon, upper (0.15%) and lower (0.10%) limits are set, and for others only an upper limit is imposed, 0.04% for phosphorus, for example.

A small sample of the steel is taken. In the spectrograph a little of this is vaporized and excited in an electric discharge so that it emits light. This light is examined in much the same way as you examined the spectrum of the mercury lamp with your spectroscope. Each element emits light of characteristic frequencies, so each element present in the steel can be identified. But the manufacturer also needs to know *how much* of each element is present. As you might expect, the higher the concentration of an element, the more intense is its emitted spectrum. The large spectrograph is able to measure the intensities of the light emitted at various frequencies. A computer linked to the spectrograph calculates the composition of the steel. The whole analysis takes less than one minute, and within three minutes of taking a sample the operator at the furnace knows what substances to add to the steel, for example manganese, and the amount needed to reach the required composition.

The furnace shown at British Steel in Rotherham has been replaced by a more modern furnace, now part of United Engineering Steels Limited. The type of furnace shown is used only for melting steel, while a second (ladle) furnace is used for adding material to produce the desired alloy product. These improvements lead to a reduction in the time to produce a batch of steel, now only 70 minutes. Improvements in sampling and analysis have also been made. Sampling of the molten steel is done automatically, as is cutting, grinding and inserting the sample in the spectrophotometer.

The interpretation of spectra was then considered. You saw that mercury vapour is very effective at absorbing the light from a mercury lamp; the vapour casts a shadow. In a similar experiment with sodium we found that this is because the atoms of an element are able to absorb light of the same frequency as that of the light that they emit.

This observation was interpreted with an electron energy-level diagram: in emission the electron jumps from one energy level down to another, and in absorption the jumps are upwards. The electronic spectrum of hydrogen can be interpreted in this way and the energy-level diagram related to the spectral lines (Section 5).

The use of absorption spectra enables us to gain information about the stars. You should have seen the Fraunhofer lines (the dark lines) in the Sun's spectrum in your observations with the spectroscope. The Sun is a rather typical star in this respect; light emitted from the hot surface of a star is absorbed by the cooler atoms that are present in the 'atmosphere' of the star. You saw how visual comparison of a selected star's spectrum with the spectra of various star types showed it to be rather like the Sun; most of the strong absorption lines were due to hydrogen. More information about the composition of the star was obtainable from the frequencies of lines in its spectrum. These frequencies were estimated by comparison with frequencies of emission lines from an argon lamp photographed on the same plate.

In the programme the plate is a *negative*, so that the *emission* lines of argon appear *dark* and the central *absorption* lines of the star appear *light*. Spectroscopists tend to use negative photographs rather than positives because black and white photographs are first taken as negatives: their use saves the bother of making a positive. This tendency demonstrates not that spectroscopists are lazy, but that they follow one of the golden rules of scientific experiments: never do more work than you have to in order to solve the problem in hand!

You then saw the temperature of the star being estimated. At higher temperatures the average energies of atoms are higher, so that the electrons in atoms occupy higher energy levels. So the relative intensities of lines corresponding to, for example absorption by hydrogen atoms, tell us the relative populations of energy levels, and in turn this tells us the star's temperature. The intensities of lines in the star's spectrum were measured with a densitometer and the result is shown in Figure 54. As you can see, most of the lines in the spectrum are due to hydrogen: like the Sun, this star consists mainly of hydrogen. As the star ages, the hydrogen is 'burned' in nuclear reactions, fusion reactions which convert hydrogen into heavier elements. In fact, the elements heavier than helium have been largely produced in this way inside stars.

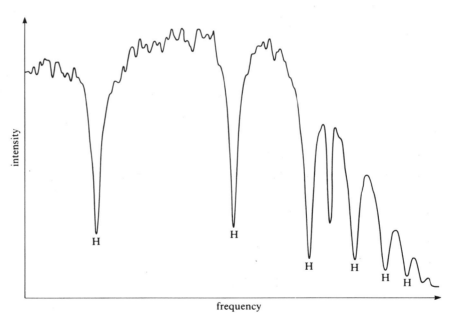

FIGURE 54   The absorption spectrum of the star η Leonis: the intensity of the light received from the star is plotted against frequency.

ACKNOWLEDGEMENT

We wish to thank Mr Lawrence Kidman for his assistance with the filming of spectral analysis of the steel sample.

APPENDIX 1   Relative atomic masses and atomic numbers of the elements

Element	Symbol	Atomic number	Relative atomic mass	Element	Symbol	Atomic number	Relative atomic mass
Actinium	Ac	89	227	Mercury	Hg	80	200.59
Aluminium	Al	13	26.981 53	Molybdenum	Mo	42	95.94
Americium	Am	95	243	Neodymium	Nd	60	144.24
Antimony	Sb	51	121.75	Neon	Ne	10	20.17
Argon	Ar	18	39.948	Neptunium	Np	93	237.048 2
Arsenic	As	33	74.921 6	Nickel	Ni	28	58.71
Astatine	At	85	210	Niobium	Nb	41	92.906
Barium	Ba	56	137.34	Nitrogen	N	7	14.006 7
Berkelium	Bk	97	247	Nobelium	No	102	254
Beryllium	Be	4	9.012 2	Osmium	Os	76	190.2
Bismuth	Bi	83	208.980	Oxygen	O	8	15.999 4
Boron	B	5	10.81	Palladium	Pd	46	106.4
Bromine	Br	35	79.909	Phosphorus	P	15	30.973 8
Cadmium	Cd	48	112.40	Platinum	Pt	78	195.09
Calcium	Ca	20	40.08	Plutonium	Pu	94	242
Californium	Cf	98	251	Polonium	Po	84	210
Carbon	C	6	12.011 15	Potassium	K	19	39.098 3
Cerium	Ce	58	140.12	Praseodymium	Pr	59	140.907 7
Caesium	Cs	55	132.905 1	Promethium	Pm	61	147
Chlorine	Cl	17	35.453	Protactinium	Pa	91	231.035 9
Chromium	Cr	24	51.996	Radium	Ra	88	226.025 4
Cobalt	Co	27	58.933 2	Radon	Rn	86	222
Copper	Cu	29	63.54	Rhenium	Re	75	186.2
Curium	Cm	96	247	Rhodium	Rh	45	102.905
Dysprosium	Dy	66	162.50	Rubidium	Rb	37	85.47
Einsteinium	Es	99	254	Ruthenium	Ru	44	101.07
Erbium	Er	68	167.26	Samarium	Sm	62	150.35
Europium	Eu	63	151.96	Scandium	Sc	21	44.955 92
Fermium	Fm	100	253	Selenium	Se	34	78.96
Fluorine	F	9	18.998 4	Silicon	Si	14	28.086
Francium	Fr	87	223	Silver	Ag	47	107.887 0
Gadolinium	Gd	64	157.25	Sodium	Na	11	22.989 8
Gallium	Ga	31	69.72	Strontium	Sr	38	87.62
Germanium	Ge	32	72.59	Sulphur	S	16	32.064
Gold	Au	79	196.967	Tantalum	Ta	73	180.948
Hafnium	Hf	72	178.49	Technetium	Tc	43	98.906 2
Helium	He	2	4.002 6	Tellurium	Te	52	127.60
Holmium	Ho	67	164.930	Terbium	Tb	65	158.924
Hydrogen	H	1	1.007 97	Thallium	Tl	81	204.37
Indium	In	49	114.82	Thorium	Th	90	232.038 1
Iodine	I	53	126.904 4	Thulium	Tm	69	168.934
Iridium	Ir	77	192.2	Tin	Sn	50	118.69
Iron	Fe	26	55.847	Titanium	Ti	22	47.90
Krypton	Kr	36	83.80	Tungsten	W	74	183.85
Lanthanum	La	57	138.91	Uranium	U	92	238.029
Lawrencium	Lr	103	257	Vanadium	V	23	50.942
Lead	Pb	82	207.2	Xenon	Xe	54	131.30
Lithium	Li	3	6.941	Ytterbium	Yb	70	173.04
Lutetium	Lu	71	174.97	Yttrium	Y	39	88.905
Magnesium	Mg	12	24.312	Zinc	Zn	30	65.37
Manganese	Mn	25	54.938 1	Zirconium	Zr	40	91.22
Mendelevium	Md	101	256				

APPENDIX 2 Electronic configurations of the elements

	1s	2s	2p	3s	3p	3d	4s	4p	4d	4f	5s	5p	5d	5f	6s	6p	6d	7s
1 H	1																	
2 He	2																	
3 Li	2	1																
4 Be	2	2																
5 B	2	2	1															
6 C	2	2	2															
7 N	2	2	3															
8 O	2	2	4															
9 F	2	2	5															
10 Ne	2	2	6															
11 Na	2	2	6	1														
12 Mg	2	2	6	2														
13 Al	2	2	6	2	1													
14 Si	2	2	6	2	2													
15 P	2	2	6	2	3													
16 S	2	2	6	2	4													
17 Cl	2	2	6	2	5													
18 Ar	2	2	6	2	6													
19 K	2	2	6	2	6		1											
20 Ca	2	2	6	2	6		2											
21 Sc	2	2	6	2	6	1	2											
22 Ti	2	2	6	2	6	2	2											
23 V	2	2	6	2	6	3	2											
24 Cr	2	2	6	2	6	5	1											
25 Mn	2	2	6	2	6	5	2											
26 Fe	2	2	6	2	6	6	2											
27 Co	2	2	6	2	6	7	2											
28 Ni	2	2	6	2	6	8	2											
29 Cu	2	2	6	2	6	10	1											
30 Zn	2	2	6	2	6	10	2											
31 Ga	2	2	6	2	6	10	2	1										
32 Ge	2	2	6	2	6	10	2	2										
33 As	2	2	6	2	6	10	2	3										
34 Se	2	2	6	2	6	10	2	4										
35 Br	2	2	6	2	6	10	2	5										
36 Kr	2	2	6	2	6	10	2	6										
37 Rb	2	2	6	2	6	10	2	6			1							
38 Sr	2	2	6	2	6	10	2	6			2							
39 Y	2	2	6	2	6	10	2	6	1		2							
40 Zr	2	2	6	2	6	10	2	6	2		2							
41 Nb	2	2	6	2	6	10	2	6	4		1							
42 Mo	2	2	6	2	6	10	2	6	5		1							
43 Tc	2	2	6	2	6	10	2	6	6		1							
44 Ru	2	2	6	2	6	10	2	6	7		1							
45 Rh	2	2	6	2	6	10	2	6	8		1							
46 Pd	2	2	6	2	6	10	2	6	10									
47 Ag	2	2	6	2	6	10	2	6	10		1							
48 Cd	2	2	6	2	6	10	2	6	10		2							
49 In	2	2	6	2	6	10	2	6	10		2	1						
50 Sn	2	2	6	2	6	10	2	6	10		2	2						
51 Sb	2	2	6	2	6	10	2	6	10		2	3						
52 Te	2	2	6	2	6	10	2	6	10		2	4						
53 I	2	2	6	2	6	10	2	6	10		2	5						
54 Xe	2	2	6	2	6	10	2	6	10		2	6						

APPENDIX 2—Continued.

	1s	2s	2p	3s	3p	3d	4s	4p	4d	4f	5s	5p	5d	5f	6s	6p	6d	7s
55 Cs	2	2	6	2	6	10	2	6	10		2	6			1			
56 Ba	2	2	6	2	6	10	2	6	10		2	6			2			
57 La	2	2	6	2	6	10	2	6	10		2	6	1		2			
58 Ce	2	2	6	2	6	10	2	6	10	2	2	6			2			
59 Pr	2	2	6	2	6	10	2	6	10	3	2	6			2			
60 Nd	2	2	6	2	6	10	2	6	10	4	2	6			2			
61 Pm	2	2	6	2	6	10	2	6	10	5	2	6			2			
62 Sm	2	2	6	2	6	10	2	6	10	6	2	6			2			
63 Eu	2	2	6	2	6	10	2	6	10	7	2	6			2			
64 Gd	2	2	6	2	6	10	2	6	10	7	2	6	1		2			
65 Tb	2	2	6	2	6	10	2	6	10	9	2	6			2			
66 Dy	2	2	6	2	6	10	2	6	10	10	2	6			2			
67 Ho	2	2	6	2	6	10	2	6	10	11	2	6			2			
68 Er	2	2	6	2	6	10	2	6	10	12	2	6			2			
69 Tm	2	2	6	2	6	10	2	6	10	13	2	6			2			
70 Yb	2	2	6	2	6	10	2	6	10	14	2	6			2			
71 Lu	2	2	6	2	6	10	2	6	10	14	2	6	1		2			
72 Hf	2	2	6	2	6	10	2	6	10	14	2	6	2		2			
73 Ta	2	2	6	2	6	10	2	6	10	14	2	6	3		2			
74 W	2	2	6	2	6	10	2	6	10	14	2	6	4		2			
75 Re	2	2	6	2	6	10	2	6	10	14	2	6	5		2			
76 Os	2	2	6	2	6	10	2	6	10	14	2	6	6		2			
77 Ir	2	2	6	2	6	10	2	6	10	14	2	6	7		2			
78 Pt	2	2	6	2	6	10	2	6	10	14	2	6	9		1			
79 Au	2	2	6	2	6	10	2	6	10	14	2	6	10		1			
80 Hg	2	2	6	2	6	10	2	6	10	14	2	6	10		2			
81 Tl	2	2	6	2	6	10	2	6	10	14	2	6	10		2	1		
82 Pb	2	2	6	2	6	10	2	6	10	14	2	6	10		2	2		
83 Bi	2	2	6	2	6	10	2	6	10	14	2	6	10		2	3		
84 Po	2	2	6	2	6	10	2	6	10	14	2	6	10		2	4		
85 At	2	2	6	2	6	10	2	6	10	14	2	6	10		2	5		
86 Rn	2	2	6	2	6	10	2	6	10	14	2	6	10		2	6		
87 Fr	2	2	6	2	6	10	2	6	10	14	2	6	10		2	6		1
88 Ra	2	2	6	2	6	10	2	6	10	14	2	6	10		2	6		2
89 Ac	2	2	6	2	6	10	2	6	10	14	2	6	10		2	6	1	2
90 Th	2	2	6	2	6	10	2	6	10	14	2	6	10		2	6	2	2
91 Pa	2	2	6	2	6	10	2	6	10	14	2	6	10	2	2	6	1	2
92 U	2	2	6	2	6	10	2	6	10	14	2	6	10	3	2	6	1	2
93 Np	2	2	6	2	6	10	2	6	10	14	2	6	10	4	2	6	1	2
94 Pu	2	2	6	2	6	10	2	6	10	14	2	6	10	6	2	6		2
95 Am	2	2	6	2	6	10	2	6	10	14	2	6	10	7	2	6		2
96 Cm	2	2	6	2	6	10	2	6	10	14	2	6	10	7	2	6	1	2
97 Bk	2	2	6	2	6	10	2	6	10	14	2	6	10	9	2	6		2
98 Cf	2	2	6	2	6	10	2	6	10	14	2	6	10	10	2	6		2
99 Es	2	2	6	2	6	10	2	6	10	14	2	6	10	11	2	6		2
100 Fm	2	2	6	2	6	10	2	6	10	14	2	6	10	12	2	6		2
101 Md	2	2	6	2	6	10	2	6	10	14	2	6	10	13	2	6		2
102 No	2	2	6	2	6	10	2	6	10	14	2	6	10	14	2	6		2
103 Lr	2	2	6	2	6	10	2	6	10	14	2	6	10	14	2	6	1	2

OBJECTIVES FOR UNITS 11–12

After you have worked through these Units, you should be able to:

1 Explain the meaning of, and use correctly, all the terms flagged in the text.

2 Represent elements, atoms, isotopes and ions using chemical symbols, given access to the information in Appendix 1. (*SAQs 1, 5 and 7*)

3 Describe evidence (for example, experiments and their results) for the existence of atoms. (*SAQ 2*)

4 Describe and interpret an experiment to determine roughly the size of an atom. (*SAQs 3 and 4*)

5 Estimate roughly the number of atoms in an object. (*SAQ 4*)

6 Describe and interpret the results of an experiment in which atomic masses are measured. (*SAQs 6 and 8*)

7 Use symbols to represent the numbers of protons, neutrons and electrons in an atom. (*SAQs 9, 11 and 12*)

8 Describe the Rutherford model of the atom, giving roughly the dimensions of the atom and the nucleus, and describe how evidence for the model was obtained. (*SAQ 10*)

9 Complete balanced equations depicting nuclear reactions. (*SAQs 14, 15 and 16*)

10 Give examples of important nuclear reactions as outlined in Section 4.

11 Determine the age of a sample containing carbon, given Figure 14 and the fraction of ^{14}C remaining in the sample. (*SAQ 13*)

12 Identify elements by using their atomic spectra. (*ITQs 1 and 2*)

13 Relate atomic spectra to energy changes on an electron energy-level diagram. (*SAQs 21 and 24*)

14 Represent or interpret on an electron energy-level diagram the energy jumps corresponding to:

(a) emission spectra;   (b) absorption spectra;

(c) photoelectron spectra;   (d) ionization.

(*SAQs 17–22 and 24; Exercise 1*)

15 Appreciate that energy changes of electrons in atoms can only correspond to differences between 'allowed' energies. (*SAQs 20 and 34*)

16 Outline a model of a light atom (one with atomic number, Z, less than 20) that is consistent with the information provided by its electronic and photoelectron spectra. (*SAQs 26–28*).

17 Estimate roughly the ionization energy of an atom, using a series of spectral lines or the electron energy-level diagram derived from atomic spectra. (*ITQ 3, SAQs 23 and 25; Exercise 2*)

18 Describe and identify experimental evidence for the existence of electron shells, subshells, electron spin and degenerate energy levels. (*SAQs 27 and 28*).

19 Relate the evidence in Objective 18 to the quantization of electron energy in the atom, and label the electron energy levels using quantum numbers. (*ITQs 4 and 6, SAQs 26, 28, 29, 30, 31, 32 and 33*)

20 Represent the electronic configuration of an element using the s–p–d–f notation or the 'box' notation, given the order of filling of subshells (Figure 47). (*ITQs 5 and 8, SAQs 35 and 36*)

21 Relate patterns in the first ionization energies of the elements to their electronic configurations. (*SAQs 37 and 38*)

22 Describe and interpret the results of an experiment in which the electronic charge is measured. (*TV*)

ITQ ANSWERS AND COMMENTS

ITQ 1 The bluish-white street lights are mercury lamps. Compare their spectrum with your sketch of the spectrum of a fluorescent mercury lamp in an office or kitchen and with Spectrum C on the colour plate.

ITQ 2 Identification of the lines is quite difficult. Three or four of the strong absorption lines that you can see in the red, blue-green and blue parts of the spectrum are lines of the hydrogen spectrum. Without further information and with the limitations of the spectroscope, it is not possible to identify any of the other lines in the solar spectrum. In fact, hydrogen accounts for about 90 per cent of the atoms in the Sun. We follow up this exercise and extend it to stars in the TV programme 'Steel, stars and spectra'.

ITQ 3 Our estimate of the frequency and uncertainty limits using Figure 22 is:

$$f = 3.27 \times 10^{15} \, \text{Hz}$$

$$E = hf$$
$$= 6.626 \times 10^{-34} \, \text{J s} \times 3.27 \times 10^{15} \, \text{Hz}$$
$$= 21.7 \times 10^{-19} \, \text{J}$$

Uncertainty in $f = \pm 0.02 \times 10^{15} \, \text{Hz}$

Uncertainty in $E = \pm 0.1 \times 10^{-19} \, \text{J}$

Therefore $E = (21.7 \pm 0.1) \times 10^{-19} \, \text{J}$

ITQ 4 Your labels should be the same as the values of n shown in the energy-level diagram in Figure 55. The lowest energy level corresponds to the highest energy peak on the right of the spectrum.

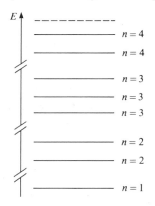

FIGURE 55 The electron energy-level diagram for krypton.

ITQ 5 Your completed diagram for neon should look like Figure 56.

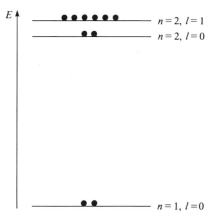

FIGURE 56 The occupation of energy levels in the neon atom.

ITQ 6 From the bottom up, the levels should be labelled: $l = 0$, $l = 0$, $l = 1$, $l = 0$, $l = 1$, $l = 2$, $l = 0$, $l = 1$. Put these labels onto Figure 55 now. You will need to refer to them later.

ITQ 7 Your diagrams for Be, Ar and Br should look like those in Figure 57.

ITQ 8 From the bottom up, the levels should be labelled 1s, 2s, 2p.

ITQ 9 All six have $n = 2$ and $l = 1$. Writing the electrons in pairs with opposite spin:

n	l	m_l	m_s
2	1	-1	$+\frac{1}{2}$
2	1	-1	$-\frac{1}{2}$
2	1	0	$+\frac{1}{2}$
2	1	0	$-\frac{1}{2}$
2	1	$+1$	$+\frac{1}{2}$
2	1	$+1$	$-\frac{1}{2}$

FIGURE 57 The occupation of energy levels in the ground state of Be, Ar and Br atoms.

ITQ 10   If you followed the procedure correctly, you should have written:

oxygen $1s^22s^22p^4$

sulphur $1s^22s^22p^63s^23p^4$

ITQ 11 $m_e = \dfrac{e}{e : m_e}$

$= \dfrac{1.6 \times 10^{-19}\,C}{1.8 \times 10^{11}\,C\,kg^{-1}}$

$= 8.9 \times 10^{-31}\,kg$

ITQ 12   The ratio is

$\dfrac{m_H}{m_e} = \dfrac{1.67 \times 10^{-27}\,kg}{8.9 \times 10^{-31}\,kg}$

$= 1.9 \times 10^3$

SAQ ANSWERS AND COMMENTS

SAQ 1   The symbol Ne can represent either the *substance* neon (a colourless gas that is present at a concentration of about 0.002% in the atmosphere), or it can represent *one atom* of neon.

SAQ 2   The spots of light on the screen of the field-ion microscope (Figure 1) indicate that the helium ions are formed at centres on the needle tip. It is reasonable to suppose that these centres are atoms of tungsten, and in fact they are.

SAQ 3   The spots in Figure 1 are about 1 mm apart and the magnification is about 10^7. Therefore an atom has a diameter of about 10^{-10} m according to this Figure. In the monolayer experiment, the diameter is reckoned to be about 10^{-9} m.

The main reason for the difference is the number of atoms in the molecules that make up the monolayer, roughly ten in fact, which puts the two results in very close agreement.

SAQ 4   Approximately 10^{26}; a hundred million million million million! The volume of a cup of tea is typically about 200 cm^3. If each atom is assumed to be a cube of length l, and $l = 10^{-8}$ cm (from SAQ 3), then

volume of atom $= l^3$

$\approx 10^{-24}\,cm^3$

So the number of atoms in a cup of tea is

$\dfrac{\text{volume of tea}}{\text{volume of atom}}$

$= \dfrac{2 \times 10^2\,cm^3}{10^{-24}\,cm^3}$

$\sim 10^{26}$

If you find it difficult to imagine a number as big as this, you are not alone. Atoms are indeed *very* small.

SAQ 5 Hg^+ denotes a mercury ion with a single positive charge, that is an atom of mercury that has lost one electron.

SAQ 6   Mercury consists of isotopes. The seven peaks in the mass spectrum indicate that naturally occurring mercury has seven isotopes.

A mass spectrometer separates a mixture of atoms according to their mass. The appearance of several peaks in the mass spectrum shows that the sample, in this case mercury, consists of several types of mercury atom, which can be distinguished only by their mass.

SAQ 7   The symbols for the isotopes present are:

$^{196}Hg, \ ^{198}Hg, \ ^{199}Hg, \ ^{200}Hg, \ ^{201}Hg, \ ^{202}Hg, \ ^{204}Hg$

Isotopes are denoted by the symbol for the element, accompanied by a superscript to show the mass number of the atom of that isotope. For example, the lightest isotope present appears to have a relative atomic mass very close to 196: hence its mass number is 196. The symbol for this isotope is therefore ^{196}Hg.

SAQ 8   Chlorine must contain significant amounts of more than one isotope.

Atoms appear to consist of particles that have masses very close to one unit of relative atomic mass. Each isotope of an atom should therefore have a relative atomic mass that is very close to a whole number. If the relative atomic mass of an element is not close to a whole number, the element must consist of a mixture of isotopes. The relative atomic mass of an element is the weighted average of the relative atomic masses of the isotopes. In fact chlorine consists of two isotopes ^{35}Cl (75.5%) and ^{37}Cl (24.5%) although you would not be expected to know this. The relative atomic mass of the element is then:

$A_r = (34.97 \times 0.755) + (36.96 \times 0.245) = 35.45$

SAQ 9   The symbols represent three different isotopes of hydrogen, each containing a different number of neutrons.

^1_1H represents an isotope containing no neutrons. It is usually just called hydrogen.

^2_1H represents an isotope containing one neutron. It is given a special name—deuterium.

^3_1H represents an isotope containing two neutrons. It is called tritium.

Remember that the subscript denotes the number of protons in the nucleus; one for a hydrogen atom. The superscript denotes the number of protons plus neutrons in the atom, that is, the mass number of the isotope.

As you can see from the relative atomic mass of natural hydrogen (1.008), it predominantly consists of the isotope $^1_1$H.

SAQ 10 The surprising result of this experiment, which revealed the presence of a small heavy nucleus with a positive charge, was the scattering of some α-particles through very large angles, occasionally back towards the source of α-particles. Only an electrostatic force acting at a very small distance would be large enough to account for this scattering. The electric charge in the atom is associated with a small body, which must be very massive in comparison to the α-particle; otherwise gold atoms would be knocked away from the foil by the α-particles. Knowing that atoms contain electrons (recall the photoelectric effect), which are very light and negatively charged, Rutherford proposed that the scattering was caused by a nucleus with a large mass (approximately the mass of the atom) and with a positive charge, which exactly balances the negative charges on the electrons.

SAQ 11

Particle	Mass number	Charge/e
proton	1	+1
neutron	1	0
H atom	1	0
α-particle	4	+2
electron	0	−1

SAQ 12 Symbols for the isotopes are:

$$^{194}_{78}\text{Pt} \qquad ^{195}_{78}\text{Pt} \qquad ^{196}_{78}\text{Pt} \qquad ^{198}_{78}\text{Pt}$$

In his experiments, Chadwick was able to determine the charge of the nucleus and hence the number of protons in the nucleus (the atomic number). For platinum, this is 78 (written as a subscript). The relative atomic masses give the mass numbers of the isotopes and hence the numbers of protons plus neutrons in the atoms. The mass number is written as a superscript.

SAQ 13 According to Figure 14, the wood is about 4900 years old. This dating process is based on the known rate of decay of $^{14}_6$C and the assumption that the natural abundance of ^{14}C has not changed with time. Since the ancient Egyptians kept accurate calendars, the age of the pyramids is usually known precisely. The Snefuru pyramid is known to be about 4800 years old, in excellent agreement with the $^{14}_6$C dating result.

SAQ 14 The other product is the neutron, $^1_0$n. This experiment proved that the neutron existed as a particle and is generally recognized as the discovery of the neutron.

To conclude that the neutron is the other product, you have to balance the equation; the total mass (sum of the mass numbers) and the total charge (the sum of the atomic numbers) must be conserved. The mass number of the product is therefore $9 + 4 - 12 = 1$. Similarly, the charge of the product is $4 + 2 - 6 = 0$.

SAQ 15 The atomic number of the product is 94. The addition of one neutron to the nucleus increases the mass number by one but does not change the atomic number. However, the resulting nucleus is unstable and it decays in two steps by emitting two electrons ($_{-1}^0$e), which increases the atomic number of the nucleus by two. The product has atomic number 94 (see Appendix 1), so it is plutonium.

Plutonium is one of the elements that does not occur naturally. The isotope produced in this reaction is $^{239}_{94}$Pu, which is itself unstable and in a reactor eventually undergoes fission to produce more neutrons and two other nuclei of lighter elements in much the same way as $^{235}_{92}$U does (see Section 4.3). Plutonium could therefore power a nuclear reactor as $^{235}_{92}$U does. Now the uranium isotope $^{238}_{92}$U is relatively stable and much more abundant than $^{235}_{92}$U, but in a reactor with $^{235}_{92}$U, it gradually becomes converted into $^{239}_{94}$Pu, which can be used as fuel in another source of nuclear power, the 'breeder' reactor.

SAQ 16 The atomic number is 98, so the product is californium.

Since both the charge and the total number of protons plus neutrons are conserved in nuclear reactions, the charge on the nucleus of the product is $92 + 6 = 98$; the nucleus contains 98 protons and is californium (see Appendix 1). Californium was first obtained in 1950 by the American scientist Glenn Seaborg at Berkeley, in California. The name of the element (and of elements 95 and 97) was chosen to honour the place where it was discovered.

SAQ 17 The energy change corresponding to the red emission line is approximately 3.03×10^{-19} J.

The red line in Spectrum B is close to 4.57×10^{14} Hz (or s^{-1}) in frequency. The energy is given by:

$$E = hf$$

So, for the red line,

$$E = (6.626 \times 10^{-34}\,\text{J s}) \times (4.57 \times 10^{14}\,\text{s}^{-1})$$

$$= 3.03 \times 10^{-19}\,\text{J}$$

Your reading of Spectrum B is probably accurate enough to allow you to be sure of only two significant figures in this answer.

SAQ 18 $2.15 \times 10^{-19} \, \text{J}$.

The highest level has an energy of $5.18 \times 10^{-19} \, \text{J}$ and the second lowest an energy of $3.03 \times 10^{-19} \, \text{J}$. The *difference* is the energy of the photon that is emitted: $2.15 \times 10^{-19} \, \text{J}$. (This is in the infrared region of the spectrum.)

SAQ 19 From $n = 1$ to $n = 2$ at $2.47 \times 10^{15} \, \text{Hz}$
From $n = 1$ to $n = 3$ at $2.92 \times 10^{15} \, \text{Hz}$
From $n = 1$ to $n = 4$ at $3.08 \times 10^{15} \, \text{Hz}$

Adding $16.34 \times 10^{-19} \, \text{J}$ to the energies of the red and blue–green photons listed in the last column of Table 5 gives the energies (relative to the lowest level, that is, $n = 1$) of the $n = 3$ and 4 levels. The energy $16.34 \times 10^{-19} \, \text{J}$ corresponds to the transition from $n = 1$ to $n = 2$.

(i) $19.37 \times 10^{-19} \, \text{J}$ for the $n = 3$ level
(ii) $20.43 \times 10^{-19} \, \text{J}$ for the $n = 4$ level

The frequency, f, of the radiation absorbed when the electron is excited from the $n = 1$ level to each of these levels is obtained by dividing this energy, E, by h:

$$f = \frac{E}{h}$$

This gives the frequencies listed above.

SAQ 20 (i) Yes. (ii) Yes. (iii) No. (iv) No. In the ground-state atom, the electron is in the level $n = 1$.

(i) Only the first of the energies listed corresponds to a difference in energy between the $n = 1$ level and a higher energy level (see Figure 19).

(ii) Absorption of $22.74 \times 10^{-19} \, \text{J}$ will excite the electron of the hydrogen atom from the $n = 1$ level into the continuum. The 'extra' $1 \times 10^{-19} \, \text{J}$ above that required for ionization will be converted into kinetic energy of the emitted electron, so that an electron in the $n = 1$ level can be excited by a photon with energy $22.74 \times 10^{-19} \, \text{J}$.

(iii) The atom cannot, however, absorb $17.5 \times 10^{-19} \, \text{J}$, since this would give it an energy intermediate between that 'allowed' in the second and third energy level. Note that the atom cannot absorb just part of the energy of the photon—it's a case of all or none.

(iv) Nor can it absorb $11.0 \times 10^{-19} \, \text{J}$, which is not enough to bring it from the ground state to the first excited state. These last two photons will *not* be absorbed by a ground-state hydrogen atom.

SAQ 21 The energy of the emitted photon is

$$E = hf$$
$$= (6.6 \times 10^{-34} \, \text{J s}) \times (1.6 \times 10^{14} \, \text{Hz})$$
$$\approx 1.1 \times 10^{-19} \, \text{J}$$

(Note: $1 \, \text{Hz} = 1 \, \text{s}^{-1}$, from Unit 10.) Comparison with a completed version of Figure 19 (i.e. Figure 62) shows that this must be due to transition of the electron from $n = 4$ to $n = 3$, because this is the transition whose energy spacing most closely corresponds to $1.1 \times 10^{-19} \, \text{J}$.

SAQ 22 (i) $21.34 \times 10^{-19} \, \text{J}$, (ii) $8.55 \times 10^{-18} \, \text{J}$, (iii) $1.92 \times 10^{-17} \, \text{J}$.

Reading from Figures 24 and 25, the frequency of the sixth line (in order of increasing frequency) is $1.29 \times 10^{16} \, \text{Hz}$ for He^+ and $2.90 \times 10^{16} \, \text{Hz}$ for Li^{2+}. These lines correspond to the jump between $n = 1$ and $n = 7$ in each case. The energy of the transition is obtained by multiplying the frequency f by h:

$$E = hf$$

For He^+

$$E = (6.626 \times 10^{-34} \, \text{J s}) \times (1.29 \times 10^{16} \, \text{Hz})$$
$$= 8.55 \times 10^{-18} \, \text{J}$$

For Li^{2+}

$$E = (6.626 \times 10^{-34} \, \text{J s}) \times (2.90 \times 10^{16} \, \text{Hz})$$
$$= 1.92 \times 10^{-17} \, \text{J}$$

For hydrogen, the energy of the $n = 1$ to $n = 7$ transition is obtained by adding $16.34 \times 10^{-19} \, \text{J}$ to the energy of the *fifth* line in Table 5 (Balmer series). This gives $21.34 \times 10^{-19} \, \text{J}$. As the seventh level is getting close to the ionization energy, we can see how this energy increases as we go from H to He^+ to Li^{2+}.

SAQ 23 The reason for the increase in ionization energy in the series H, He^+, Li^{2+} is the increase in electrostatic attraction between the electron and the nucleus, whose positive charge increases as we go across the series. If the distance between the electron and nucleus were the same in all three cases, application of Coulomb's law would predict, for example, that the ionization energy of He^+ should be twice that of H because the charge on the He nucleus is $+2$ as against $+1$ for H. However, the electron is much closer to the nucleus in the case of He^+ than it is in H, which further increases the electrostatic attraction. It is actually about four times more difficult to ionize He^+ than H.

SAQ 24 Figure 58 shows the transitions:

(a) arrows 1 or 2;
(b) arrows 3, 4 or 5 (but see comment below);
(c) arrow 6;
(d) arrow 7.

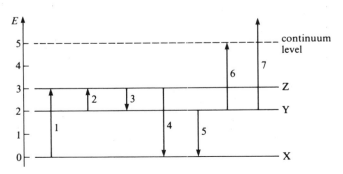

FIGURE 58 The transitions 1 to 7 for the hypothetical element pandemonium.

(a) An absorption occurs when an atom absorbs a photon and an electron is excited from a lower electron energy level to a higher electron energy level. In the ground state, only levels X and Y are occupied. The only higher level shown is Z. So the only absorptions possible are X → Z (arrow 1) and Y → Z (arrow 2). The transition X → Y cannot occur because in the ground state the level Y is already fully occupied.

(b) Emission occurs when an electron drops from a higher electron energy level to a lower electron energy level. It can only occur from excited states of the atom, in this case when at least one electron is in level Z. The resulting electron 'jump' will depend on the level that contains the vacancy (the ability to accept the electron now in level Z). If this is level Y, then emission 3 can occur. If it is level X, a transition from either level Z (arrow 4) or level Y (arrow 5) can occur.

(c) The first ionization energy is the energy required to excite an electron from level Y to the continuum level (arrow 6).

(d) A photoelectron results when an atom absorbs a photon and emits an electron. The photon with 4 energy units has insufficient energy to ionize an electron in level X. Ionization from level Y can occur (arrow 7). The length of the arrow represents the photon's energy. So the kinetic energy of the photoelectron is $4 - 3 = 1$ energy unit.

SAQ 25 The lowest ionization energy is 3 energy units.

The lowest ionization energy is the energy difference between the continuum level and the highest-occupied electron energy level in the ground-state atom (level Y):

$$I = 5 - 2 = 3 \text{ energy units}$$

SAQ 26 The peaks in the photoelectron spectrum (A, B, C, D) are the subshells 1s, 2s, 2p and 3s, respectively. The number of electrons in each subshell is two in 1s, two in 2s, six in 2p and two in 3s. The electronic configuration is $1s^2 2s^2 2p^6 3s^2$.

From ITQ 7 you know the order of filling subshells. The sequence 1s, 2s, 2p, 3s gives the labels for the first four subshells, and the relative ionization energies indicate that there are two subshells in the $n = 2$ shell, thus supporting this conclusion. An s subshell can hold up to two electrons and a p subshell can hold up to six. Since an atom of magnesium contains twelve electrons, each of the four subshells must be full.

SAQ 27 The production of photoelectrons with discrete energies (only five peaks) shows that the electrons in the atom have discrete energies. From the relationship between energy and distance (Coulomb's law), we conclude that the electrons are arranged in a shell-like structure. The ionization energies of argon fall into three groups: A; B and C; D and E; this indicates that there are three shells occupied by electrons in the argon atom. In the outermost two shells the presence of more than one peak in the photoelectron spectrum shows the existence of subshells.

SAQ 28 An electron energy-level diagram for argon can be obtained simply by turning the photoelectron spectrum through 90° (Figure 59). Each peak in the spectrum corresponds to a subshell that contains at least one electron; the highest ionization energy corresponds to the innermost electrons.

In the electron energy-level diagram (as in the spectrum) the levels are arranged in groups. These groups are the electron shells, which are labelled with the principal quantum number, n. This quantum number has integral values from 1 upwards, as in Figure 59.

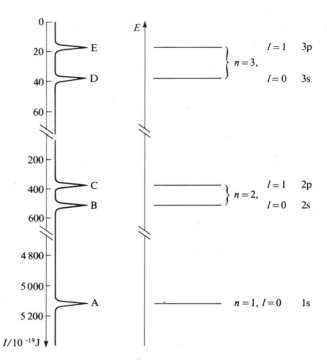

FIGURE 59 The photoelectron spectra and corresponding labelled electron energy-level diagram for argon.

Within the shells, the existence of subshells is revealed by the closely spaced peaks within each group in the photoelectron spectrum. The subshells are labelled with a second quantum number, l. This can have values from zero to $(n - 1)$, so that within a shell there can be n subshells. Evidently, one subshell is unoccupied in the $n = 3$ shell of argon. The values of l are shown in Figure 59. For historical reasons a letter is often used to label the subshells according to the value of l: s for $l = 0$; p for $l = 1$; d for $l = 2$. The levels in Figure 59 are therefore labelled 1s, 2s, 2p, 3s, 3p.

SAQ 29 (i) and (iii), no effect; (ii) Na splits into two beams.

As you have learnt in Section 6.1, neon's ten electrons *fill* the 1s, 2s and 2p shells. All electron spins are paired, and there is no resultant magnetic effect. Also, you will have deduced that all occupied levels in krypton are full, so there are no unpaired spins to interact with a magnetic field.

However, sodium has eleven electrons, so clearly at least one of these must be unpaired. In your energy-level exercise in Figure 35, only the electron in the 3s level is unpaired. Consequently, we would expect the

Na beam to split into two beams in a non-uniform magnetic field corresponding to (i) clockwise and (ii) anticlockwise spinning of the 3s electron.

SAQ 30 Application of a magnetic field causes the 1s level of atomic hydrogen to split into two levels, as we saw in Figure 44. For exactly the same reason the 2s level should also be split into two levels (Figure 60).

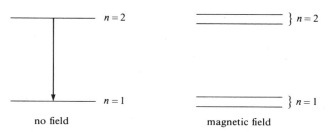

no field   magnetic field

FIGURE 60   Splitting of hydrogen energy levels in a magnetic field.

There are now four electron energy levels between which we could imagine that transitions might take place, so it is likely that more than one emission line will be observed. Although you could have no way of knowing this, only two of the possible four transitions are allowed, so the single line in the absence of a magnetic field splits into two when a strong magnetic field is applied.

SAQ 31 There should be no observed effect. Unlike hydrogen, helium has no unpaired electrons in the ground state $(1s^2)$. If there is also no magnetic effect due to electron spin in the excited state $(1s^1 2s^1)$ because the spins in the 1s and 2s levels are opposed, the presence of a magnetic field should have no effect on either state of the atom.

SAQ 32 All four electrons in the beryllium atom are paired; two in the 1s shell and two in the 2s subshell. There are no unpaired spins to produce any magnetic effect, and so this atomic beam is undeflected in an inhomogeneous magnetic field.

SAQ 33 It contains 7 orbitals. In this case $2l + 1 = 7$.

SAQ 34 There are 18 electrons in the $n = 3$ shell:

two electrons in the $l = 0$ (s subshell);

six electrons in the $l = 1$ (p subshell) in three degenerate orbitals with $m_l = +1, 0$ or -1;

ten electrons in the $l = 2$ (d subshell) in five degenerate orbitals with $m_l = +2, +1, 0, -1$ or -2.

The electronic configuration of the $n = 3$ shell is thus $3s^2 3p^6 3d^{10}$.

SAQ 35 The electronic configuration of nitrogen is represented by

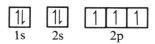

From the discussion of the four quantum numbers (Section 8.2), you can conclude that the arrangement of boxes representing orbitals is as shown. Arrows representing the electrons (nitrogen has seven) are placed in the boxes, beginning with the lowest-energy orbitals. Each box representing an orbital can accommodate a maximum of two electrons of different spin (see Section 7) represented by up and down arrows. When a choice of boxes representing orbitals of the same energy (degenerate levels) is available, as for 2p, Hund's rule states that there should be a maximum number of unpaired electrons. Hence, for nitrogen the three 2p electrons each occupy different orbitals as shown above.

SAQ 36 If you wrote for the electronic configuration of copper:

$$1s^2 2s^2 2p^6 3s^2 3p^6 4s^2 3d^9$$

then you applied the rules outlined in Section 9 correctly. Copper has an atomic number of 29 and the atom contains 29 electrons. These electrons are placed in boxes which represent orbitals. The boxes are arranged in order of energy.

However, you saw in Section 9 that as the number of levels increases their energies get closer. For chromium, the 3d and 4s levels are so close that both levels are only partially occupied. The same is true for copper. Its electronic configuration is:

$$1s^2 2s^2 2p^6 3s^2 3p^6 4s^1 3d^{10}$$

Copper and chromium are the only exceptions to the general rule that the 4s subshell fills before the 3d subshell.

SAQ 37 The sharp maximum at helium corresponds to a full 1s shell. The very sharp maxima that occur for the gaseous elements Ne, Ar and Kr all correspond to the seemingly stable arrangement of outermost electrons $s^2 p^6$, in which the s and p subshells are full. It seems likely that xenon continues this trend. If so, xenon has the outer electronic configuration $5s^2 5p^6$. Therefore, we conclude that five electron shells are occupied in xenon.

SAQ 38 Xenon has the most easily removed outer electron. As you will discover in Units 13–14, when some elements react, they often do so by their atoms gaining, losing or sharing electrons. Xenon does react to form compounds, whereas helium, neon and argon are not known to form compounds.

ANSWERS TO EXERCISES

EXERCISE 1

Your diagram of energy levels and transitions for the Balmer series shown by arrows should resemble Figure 61, with arrows depicting the transitions that give rise to three of the spectral series.

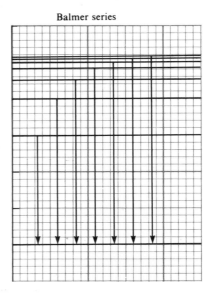

Balmer series

FIGURE 61   The energy levels of the hydrogen atom as deduced for the Balmer series (1 cm = 10^{-19} J).

EXERCISE 2

The plot extended to $n = 12$ is shown in Figure 63. The values that we estimated from this plot are:

$$E_{10} = 21.60 \times 10^{-19} \, \text{J}$$

$$E_{12} = 21.70 \times 10^{-19} \, \text{J}$$

Extrapolation of the plot in Figure 25 gives a value of $I = 21.8 \times 10^{-19}$ J with an uncertainty of 0.1×10^{-19} J. Extrapolation is not an easy procedure, and your estimates may be different.

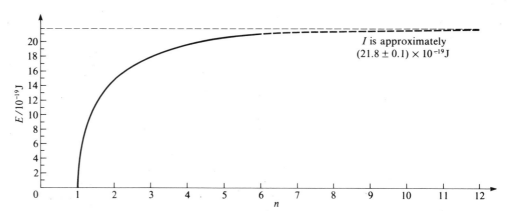

I is approximately $(21.8 \pm 0.1) \times 10^{-19}$ J

FIGURE 63   Plot of energy against principal quantum number, n, for hydrogen.

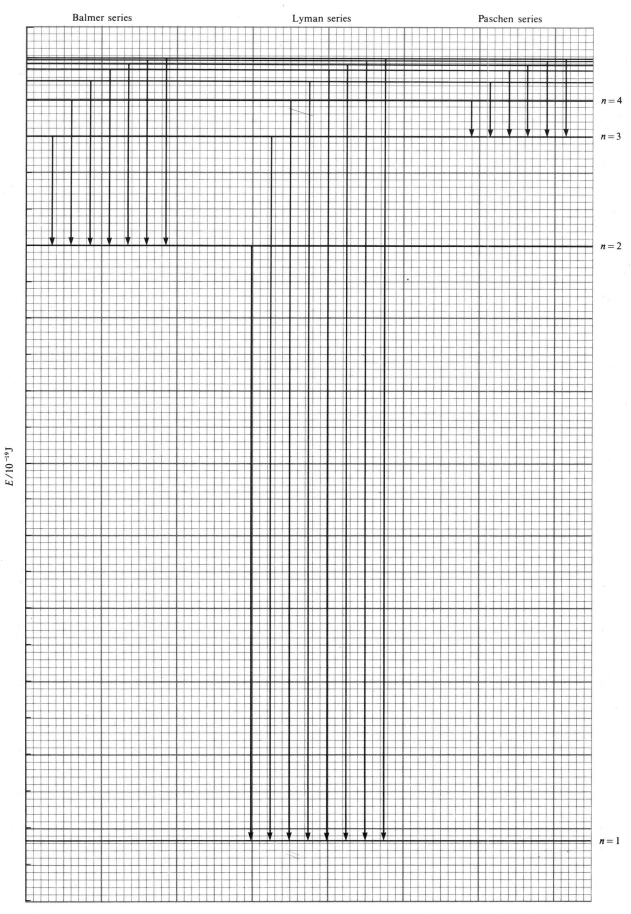

FIGURE 62   Energy levels for hydrogen and the transitions that produce three series of lines (1 cm = 10^{-19} J).

INDEX FOR UNITS 11–12

Spelling and vocabulary

Workbook

Ages
5–6

SCHOLASTIC
ENGLISH SKILLS

Spelling and vocabulary

Scholastic Education, an imprint of Scholastic Ltd
Book End, Range Road, Witney, Oxfordshire, OX29 0YD
Registered office: Westfield Road, Southam,
Warwickshire CV47 0RA

www.scholastic.co.uk

© 2016, Scholastic Ltd

5 6 7 8 9   6 7 8 9 0 1 2 3 4 5

British Library Cataloguing-in-Publication Data
A catalogue record for this book is available from the British Library.

ISBN 978-1407-14188-6
Printed by Ashford Colour Press

Author
Alison Milford

Editorial
Rachel Morgan, Anna Hall, Jenny Wilcox, Red Door Media

Design
Tracey Camden, Neil Salt and Nicolle Thomas

Cover Design
Nicolle Thomas

Illustration
Cathy Hughes

Cover Illustration
Eddie Rego

Contents

How to use this book

- *Scholastic English Skills Workbooks* help your child to practise and improve their skills in English.

- The content is divided into topics. Find out what your child is doing in school and dip into the practice activities as required.

- Keep the working time short and come back to an activity if your child finds it too difficult. Ask your child to note any areas of difficulty. Don't worry if your child does not 'get' a concept first time, as children learn at different rates and content is likely to be covered at different times throughout the school year.

- Check your child's answers at www.scholastic.co.uk/ses/spelling.

- Give lots of encouragement, complete the 'How did you do' for each activity and the progress chart as your child finishes each chapter.

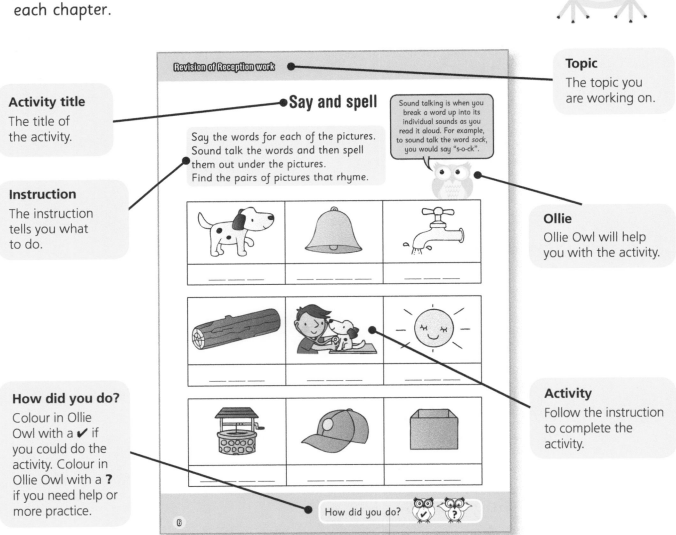

Topic
The topic you are working on.

Activity title
The title of the activity.

Instruction
The instruction tells you what to do.

Ollie
Ollie Owl will help you with the activity.

How did you do?
Colour in Ollie Owl with a ✔ if you could do the activity. Colour in Ollie Owl with a ? if you need help or more practice.

Activity
Follow the instruction to complete the activity.

If you need help, ask an adult!

What sound do I make?

Look at the cards and say the sounds.

s	a	t	p
i	n	m	d
g	o	c	k
j	e	u	r
h	b	f	qu
l	v	w	x
y	z		

Put letter sounds together to make words. How many can you make?

How did you do?

Say and spell

Say the words for each of the pictures.
Sound talk the words and then spell
them out under the pictures.
Find the pairs of pictures that rhyme.

Sound talking is when you break a word up into its individual sounds as you read it aloud. For example, to sound talk the word *sock*, you would say "s-o-ck".

How did you do?

Word ladders

Sound talk the words below. Change one letter at a time to make a new word using the letters in the list.
Try to return to the first word again.

r	l	p	g	t	e	a

r	a	t
r	a	g

Start by changing the letter at the beginning or end of the word. The middle of the word could have an **a** or **e**.

How did you do?

Gallery mix up

The letters for the names of these items are mixed up.
Look at the pictures and sound talk each word.
Write the letters in the right order in the boxes.

1.

   t   a   c

2.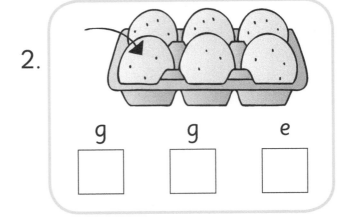

   g   g   e

3.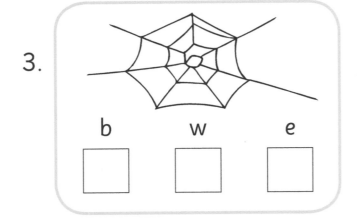

   b   w   e

4.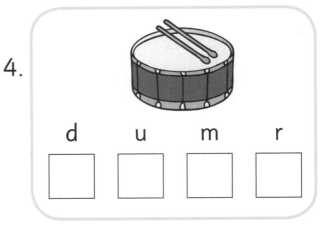

   d   u   m   r

5.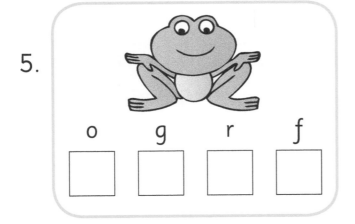

   o   g   r   f

6.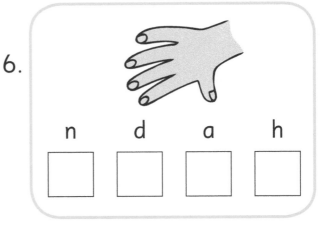

   n   d   a   h

How did you do?

On the ship

There are five words that have the /**sh**/ sound.

Look at the pictures and sound talk the words. Draw arrows to put the **sh** objects into the ship.

 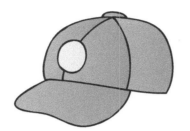 

  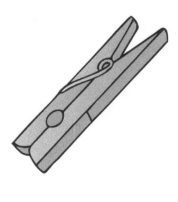

How did you do?

Kite fun

Write the missing letters to complete the words on the kites. Then draw the strings to match each kite with the right child.
Write the missing letters in the words.

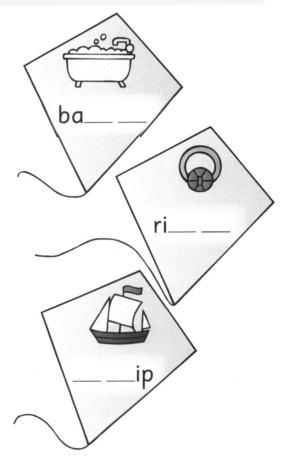

ba___ ___

ri___ ___

___ ___ip

Write the missing letters in the sentences.

1. Mila is having fun on the swi_____.

2. I love to eat fi_____ and _____ips.

How did you do?

Rhyming fun

Say the rhyming caption aloud before you write it down.

The seal ate a meal rhymes.
Write a rhyming caption underneath each picture that uses the sound in the box.

ee

_____

ow

_____

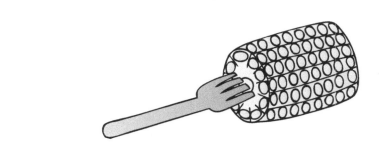

or

_____

How did you do?

Book names

Read the names on the books. Underline all the **oo** words in one colour and the **ar** words in another colour.

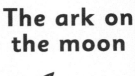
The ark on the moon

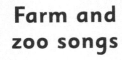
Farm and zoo songs

Two arms and one foot
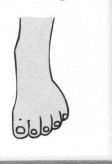

Good tools for cars

Make up two more book names using some of the **ay** and **oa** words in the box. Draw pictures to go with the names.

play   day   hay   way   stay   bay   clay   tray
goat   coat   moat   road   coach   goal

How did you do?

The runaway train

Read the rhyme. Underline all the **ai** words in one colour and the **igh** words in another colour. Write them in the correct boxes.

Oh no!
The runaway train
Has gone left
And not right!

The runaway train
Is tooting all night.

The runaway train
Is not going to wait.

So let's turn off the light.
Choo Choo!

ai	igh

See if you can add two more **ai** words and two **igh** words of your own.

How did you do?

13

Rhyming partners

Match the words from the box with words that rhyme from the beach huts. Write them under the rhyming word.

test   sand   camp   bust   hump

Sound talk each word and listen to the rhyming sounds of the two last letters. Once you have sorted the words, see if you can add two more of your own rhyming words to each hut.

lamp
_____
_____
_____

band
_____
_____
_____

jump
_____
_____
_____

best
_____
_____
_____

gust
_____
_____
_____

How did you do?

Add a letter

Read the words below. Then add **c**, **p** or **g** at the beginning to make different words.

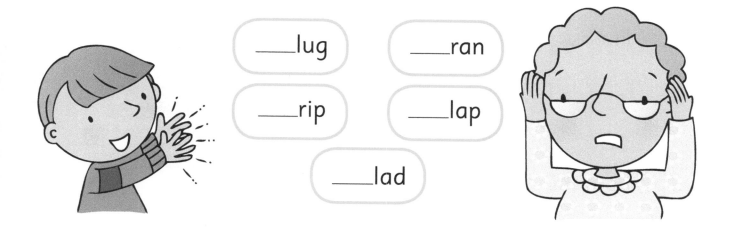

____lug   ____ran

____rip   ____lap

____lad

Write some sentences using the new words.

Fill the gaps

Fill in the gaps in the sentences. Use the picture clues to help you.

1. I like camping in my _____.

2. The baby bird fell out of its _____.

3. There are three ducks swimming on the _____.

4. I sleep on the top _____.

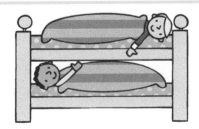

5. I bought some _____ and bread at the shop.

How did you do?

Alphabet body

Use this alphabet box to help you put the words in the right order.

a b c d e f g h i j k l m n o p q r s t u v w x y z

Write the body words in alphabetical order. Then draw lines to match each word to the correct body part.

head	_arm_
knee	_____
arm	_____
foot	_____
eye	_____
neck	_____
leg	_____
teeth	_____

How did you do?

17

Animal phonemes

Make sure you only have one sound in each square.

Sound talk the animal words below. Count the sounds in each word and write them in the correct frame.

cat   fox   thrush   rabbit   lion   fish

Remember that sounds like **th** and **sh** are made up of more than one letter even though they only make one sound.

c		a		t

How did you do?

Word wall castles

Put the words from the box into the correct word walls.
Then add one more word to each word wall.

dress	back	bell	stuff	cliff	stiff
mess	duck	hill	rock	well	fuss

How did you do?

Words ending in nk

Write the missing **nk** words in the gaps.

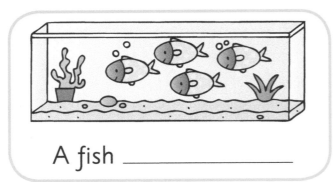

A fish _____

An elephant's _____

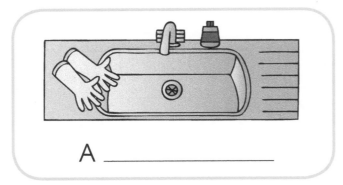

A _____

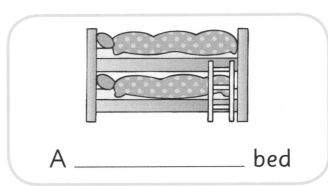

A _____ bed

A cold _____

A _____

Use some of the words above to complete these sentences.

1. I saw a seahorse in the fish _____.

2. The elephant picked up a stick with her _____.

3. There are a lot of plates in the _____.

How did you do?

Which picture?

The letters **p** and **h** together make the /**f**/ sound. The letters **w** and **h** together make the /**w**/ sound.

Add **ph** or **wh** to complete the words below.
Match the word to the correct picture.

dol___ ___in

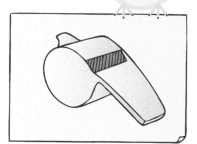

___ ___ale

___ ___one

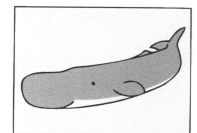

___ ___eel

tro___ ___y

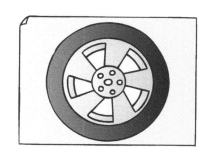

___ ___istle

Which picture do you like the best?

I like the picture of a _____ because _____

_____

How did you do?

21

Words with qu

Read the silly poem below.
Underline the words that begin with **qu**.

Cora the queen rode,
her new quad bike,
down to feed the ducks.
The bike was quick,
but not very quiet,
which made the ducks
go quack!

Use the words in the box to answer these questions.

| queen | quack | queue | quilt |

1. What sound does a duck make? _____

2. What do we line up in? _____

3. What can we put on our bed to keep warm? _____

4. Who wears a crown? _____

Write a quiz question using one of the **qu** words.

_____

How did you do?

Catch the tch words

The /**ch**/ sound can be spelled as **tch** if it comes after a vowel letter.

Use the letters in the balls to make **tch** words.

__c__ __a__ tch

___ ___tch

___ ___ ___tch

___ ___tch

___ ___tch

___ ___tch

Use some of the **tch** words above to write your own sentence.

_____

_____

How did you do?

Cave rescue

Underline the words that end with a /**v**/ sound.

> If a word ends with a /**v**/ sound, we add the letter **e** to the end of the word. For example: **live**.

1. This cave is dark.

2. I have a good torch.

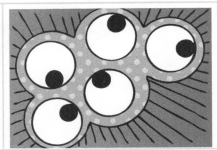

3. I can see five big eyes.

4. It is the Wave Monster!

5. Help! Somebody save us!

6. Super Steve is on his way.

Circle the incorrect spelling in each line.
Write the correct spelling.

div	drive	stove	_____
glove	giv	hive	_____
love	above	liv	_____

How did you do?

Kites

Colour in the kites with words that have the /**k**/ sound.
One has been done for you.

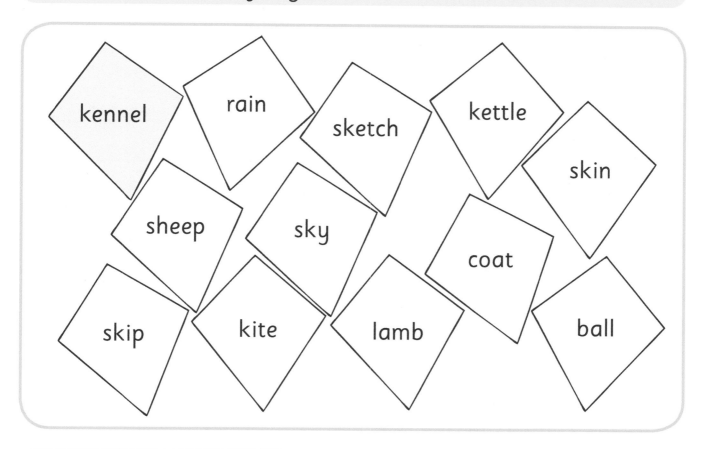

Use the /**k**/ words to complete these sentences.

1. We can make hot water in a _____.

2. I love flying my red _____.

3. Can you see the airplane in the _____?

4. Sam and Bella want to _____ around the park.

How did you do?

Riddles

Bella has written some riddles. Write the answers below next to the correct riddle.

| key | waves | hive | kennel | pitch | hutch | cave |

Riddle	Answer
1. A dog can live in one.	
2. A pet rabbit can live in one.	
3. Bees live in one of these.	
4. Bears can live in one of these.	
5. The sea has many of these.	
6. Footballers play on this.	
7. We can open a door with this.	

How did you do?

Match the sound

See if you can think of any more words to add to each column.

Say the sounds at the top of the table. Then write the words below in the correct column.

/ai/	/ee/	/igh/	/oa/	/oo/
train	sheep	light	coat	zoo

Sound talk each word to help you hear and match the right sounds.

play beach ~~train~~ pie tree blue ~~light~~

cake theme me slow tight rain field time

chew ~~sheep~~ home ~~coat~~ moon toe goat

flute pony ~~zoo~~

How did you do?

ee, ea or ie?

Add in **ee**, **ea** or **ie** to complete the words.

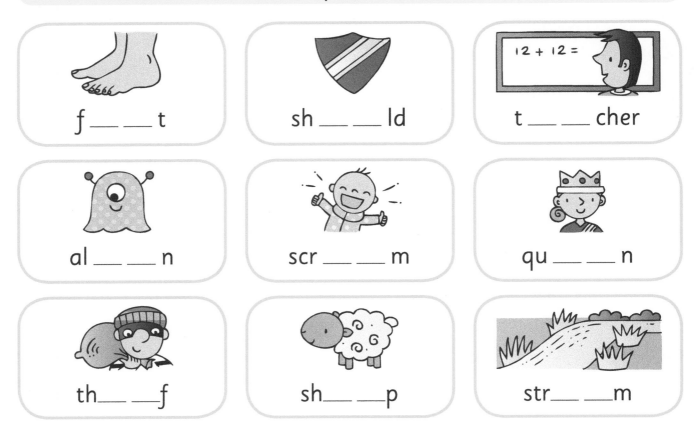

f __ __ t

sh __ __ ld

t __ __ cher

al __ __ n

scr __ __ m

qu __ __ n

th __ __ f

sh __ __ p

str __ __ m

Write the words you have made in the correct boxes.

ee	ea	ie

How did you do?

The snail on the tray

Say the rhyme. Underline words with **ai** in one colour.
Underline words with **ay** in another colour.

The snail on the tray

Today, I met a snail,
Who liked to fly on a tray.
It splashed around in the rain,
And rolled about in the hay.

It took a ride on a train,
Made an igloo out of clay,
It covered my room in paint,
And asked if it could stay!

Write the words you have underlined in the correct boxes.

ai	ay

How did you do?

Blow the foam

Words with **ow**, **oe** and **oa** share the long /**oa**/ sound.

Read the words in the foam bubbles. Underline the letters that make the long /**oa**/ sound. Some have been done for you.

tow goat blow low foam

oboe doe

toast Joe

Which is the correct spelling for each picture?
Write it on the lines underneath.

crow   croow

_____

cooat   coat

_____

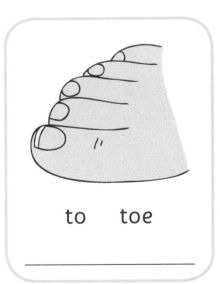

to   toe

_____

How did you do?

30

/oo/, /ue/ and /ew/

Finish the sentences using the words in the word banks.

> shampoo   kangaroo   igloo

1. An ice house is called an _____.

2. A _____ is very good at jumping.

3. We can wash our hair with _____.

> glue   blue   queue

4. I need the _____ to stick on
    my puppet's eyes.

5. There was a _____ at the bus stop.

6. I have _____ walls in my bedroom.

> stew   blew   crew

7. The pirate _____ dug for gold.

8. The wind _____ the tree down.

9. The giant made a big pot of
    carrot _____.

How did you do?

igh or ie?

Look at the spellings closely. Which looks correct?

Choose the correct words to fill in the gaps.

1. The moon comes out at _____. (niet/night)

2. I love eating apple _____. (pie/pigh)

3. Please turn off the _____. (light/liet)

4. My dad has a new spotty _____. (tigh/tie)

5. The hill was very _____. (high/hie)

6. Let's _____ (lie/ligh) on the grass to watch clouds.

Write the words in the correct boxes below.

igh	ie

Circle the words that have the /ie/ sound.

pie   knight   hit   tie   bright   igloo

How did you do?

Theme park fun

Add the missing letters **e–e** to the words on the wheel.

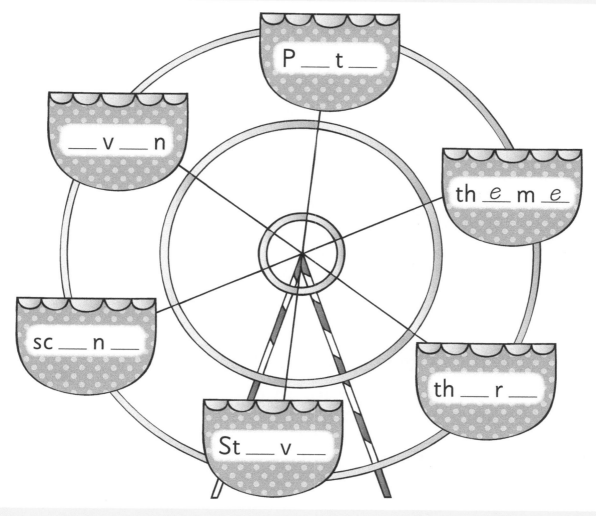

Use some of the words to complete these sentences.

1. I can see _____ on the roundabout.

2. _____ are a lot of candy floss stalls.

3. This _____ park is fun!

4. Look at this pirate _____ from the film.

How did you do?

Words with a–e

Add the missing letters **a–e** to the words below.

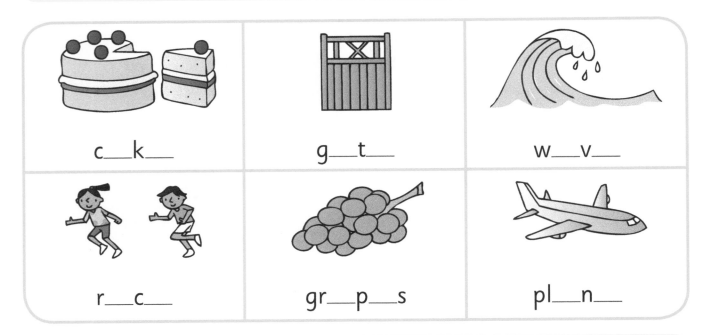

c__k__	g__t__	w__v__
r__c__	gr__p__s	pl__n__

Read and say the words below.
Underline the two letters that make the /**ai**/ sound.

bake   shape   game   cave   late

Write the **a–e** words above in the correct boxes below.
Add one more **a–e** word to each box.

ake	ate	ame	ave	ape

How did you do?

Match the pictures

Add the missing letters that make the /**oa**/ sound to the words below.
Match the words to the pictures.

In words like *stone* the letters **o** and **e** make the /**oa**/ sound.

r___s___

b___n___

sm__k__

h___m___

sl__p__

r__p__

Use the words in the box to complete the sentences.

home   woke   those

1. Pip wanted to go _____.

2. A rabbit just ate all of _____ carrots.

3. The prince _____ up Sleeping Beauty.

How did you do?

Using u–e

Add in the missing letters **u–e** to the words below.

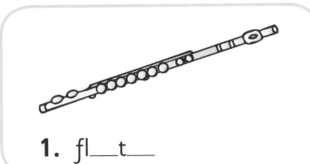

1. fl__t__

2. m__l__

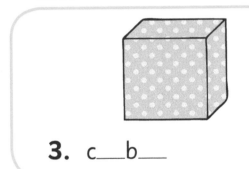

3. c__b__

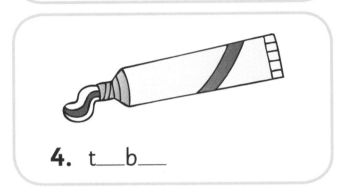

4. t__b__

Circle the words with the correct spelling.
Write the correct word in the spaces.

My birthday is on the 4th of _____. (June/Joon)

I got a _____ (huge/hewg) birthday card.

My present looked like a _____. (coob/cube)

Inside, was a small _____. (flute/floot)

I used it to play a _____. (toon/tune)

How did you do?

Spell words with i–e

Read each of these words aloud. Cover one word at a time and spell it out on the lines below. Then uncover the word and check your spelling.

Look for the letters **i** and **e** in the words. They make the /**igh**/ sound.

like	tile	pine
hide	ripe	life
chime	pile	pipe
pike	shine	tide
line	wife	time

_____   _____   _____

_____   _____   _____

_____   _____   _____

_____   _____   _____

How did you do?

Phoneme families

You could play this as a game with up to 5 players. Each player picks one of the long vowel sounds, and then all the players race to find the words that contain their vowel sound.

Pick one of the five long vowel sounds.
In one minute, find four words that match the sound.
Then cover the words and spell them on a separate piece of paper.

| /ai/ | /ee/ | /igh/ | /oa/ | /oo/ |

rope	these	threw	Pete
rain	coat	ride	glue
night	made	toe	pie
tree	flute	peach	blow
food	day	cake	kite

How did you do?

Phoneme pyramids

Sort the words into the correct word walls.

Each word wall has a different long vowel sound. Think about the different ways of spelling each sound.

sheep   cue   pie   beat   night   cube   kite

toe   theme   home   goat   time   thief   boat

mow   tree   blue

stew   tie   blew

/oo/

/igh/

/ee/

/oa/

How did you do?

39

Words with oi or oy

Add **oy** or **oi** to complete these words.

Both **oy** and **oi** make the /oi/ sound.
You can find **oy** at the end of words such as *toy*.
You can find **oi** in the middle of words such as *coin*.

b__ __

b__ __l

p__ __nt

t__ __

Underline words with **oy** in one colour and underline words with **oi** in another colour.

There once was a pirate called Troy,
Who had a loud parrot called Roy.
It would annoy the sea snake,
Who came out of its coil
And covered the parrot with oil.

How did you do?

Words with the /ur/ sound

Read the words below aloud. Underline the letters that make the /**ur**/ sound. Some have been done for you.

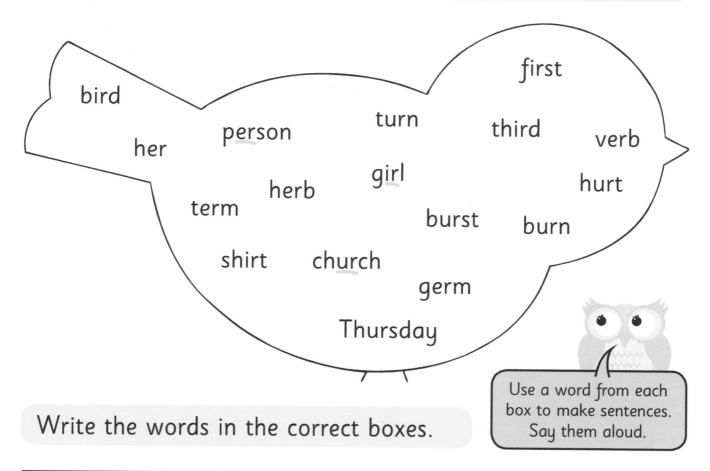

bird

her

person

term

herb

shirt

turn

girl

church

burst

germ

Thursday

first

third

verb

hurt

burn

Use a word from each box to make sentences. Say them aloud.

Write the words in the correct boxes.

ir	er	ur

How did you do?

Fun sentences

Read these sentences aloud. Listen for the **ore**, **or**, **aw** and **au** words. Underline them.

The goat went to the store to buy more apple cores.

The horse had torn its best shorts.

The dinosaur had tea with Alex the astronaut.

The monster saw the cat on the lawn and shook its paw.

Add the words you have underlined to the correct box below.

Use the words in the boxes to make up your own fun sentences. Write them on a separate piece of paper.

ore	or	au	aw
shore	for	August	yawn
sore	born	autumn	claw
snore	worn	author	straw

How did you do?

Riddles

Write the missing letters to complete the words.

| ir | aw | oy | oi | ur | or |

t____ ____

b____ ____d

c____ ____n

b____ ____n

p____ ____

h____ ____se

Use the words above to answer these riddles.

1. Children like to play with me.   _____

2. I can be used to buy things.   _____

3. I have feathers and wings.   _____

4. Wood can do this.   _____

5. I have a mane and a long tail.   _____

6. A cat has four of these.   _____

How did you do?

ow and ou pictures

Add **ou** or **ow** to the words in the captions.

A cl____n
with a cr____n.

A m____se in
the gr____nd.

An ____l on
a h____se.

Going d____n
a tall t____er.

Write your own funny caption using some of the words below. Draw a picture to go with it.

towel	mouse
town	house
shout	out
cow	down

_____

How did you do?

Rocket words

Use the letters in the planets to make some **air** and **are** words. Write the words in the rockets.

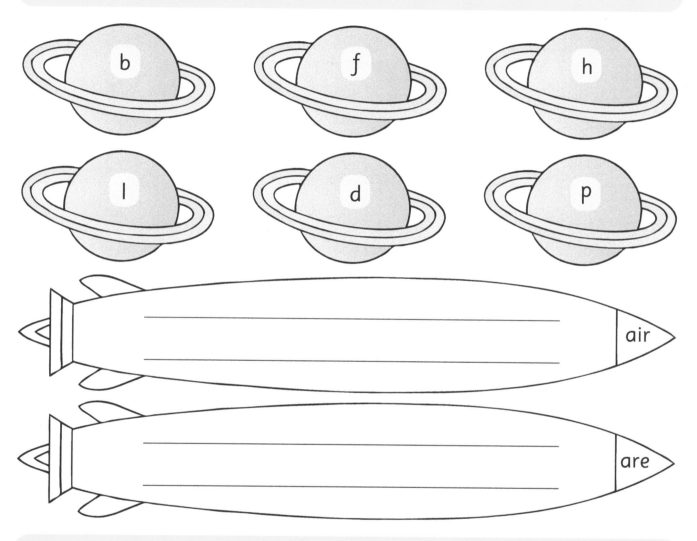

Use two of the letters from the planets to complete the /**air**/ words on the UFOs.

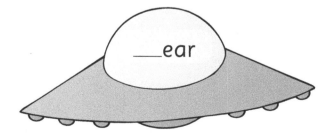

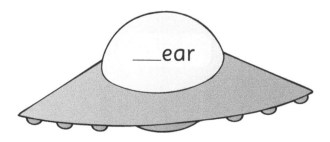

How did you do?

45

A barn and an ear

Circle the words in the barn that have an /**ar**/ sound.

barn   jam

car   lamb

scarf

harp

saw   park

rain   tart

Use some of the /**ar**/ words to complete these sentences.

1. Ava put on her spotty hat and _____.

2. The cows are in the big red _____.

3. I love eating my nan's treacle _____.

Add the letters in the left box to **ear** and make six words that have the /**ear**/ sound. Write them in the box below.

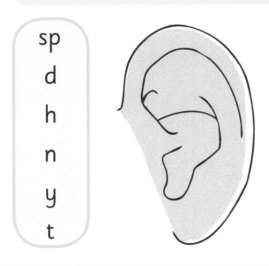

sp
d
h
n
y
t

ear words
spear

How did you do?

Know your sounds game

Roll a dice and move your counter.
Say the sound and then the word in the square.
Cover the word and spell it.

This is a game for two to four people. The winner is the first one to get to the end. If you don't get the spelling correct, miss a go.

1	2	3	4	5
/ou/	/ou/	/air/	/air/	/air/
clown	mouse	bear	chair	care
10	9	8	7	6
/air/	/ou/	/ou/	/ear/	/ar/
wear	mouth	cow	ear	car
11	12	13	14	15
/air/	/air/	/ar/	/ear/	/ou/
fair	share	shark	spear	crown
20	19	18	17	16
/ou/	/air/	/air/	/ar/	/ear/
cloud	pear	hair	barn	near

How did you do?

In Tom's head

Help Tom spell these /**ea**/ words.

Say the word *head*. Can you hear the /**ea**/ sound in the word? Say the /**ea**/ sound aloud.

f_____ther

thr____ ____d

br____ ____d

bedspr____ ____d

h____ ____d

Use some of the words to complete these sentences.

1. My _____ is on top of my bed.

2. I found a blue peacock _____ on the grass.

Write your own sentence using one of the other words.

_____

How did you do?

Rook's cookbook

Say the rhyme. Underline all the **oo** words.

A big black rook,
Opened a book,
To take a look,
For something to cook.

Worms seemed good,
Or ants from the wood,
But the chimney shook,
So the rook got soot!

Write the **oo** words on the cookbook below. Add in two more of your own **oo** words.

How did you do?

er words

Add the missing **er** to the words below.

Say the word *farmer*. Can you hear the /**er**/ sound at the end of the word?

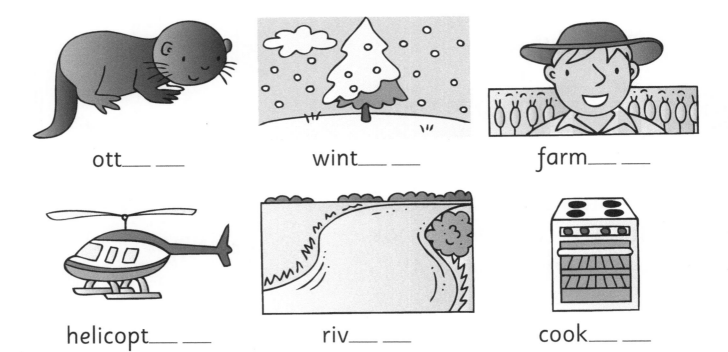

ott___ ___

wint___ ___

farm___ ___

helicopt___ ___

riv___ ___

cook___ ___

Complete these sentences using **er** words.

helicopter   sister   under   over   water   winter

1. An otter can swim _____ the _____.

2. The _____ flew _____ the trees.

3. My _____ has a new coat for _____.

How did you do?

Totem pole words

How many **ea**, **oo** and **er** words can you add to the totem poles?

Use some of the words from each box to make sentences. Say them aloud.

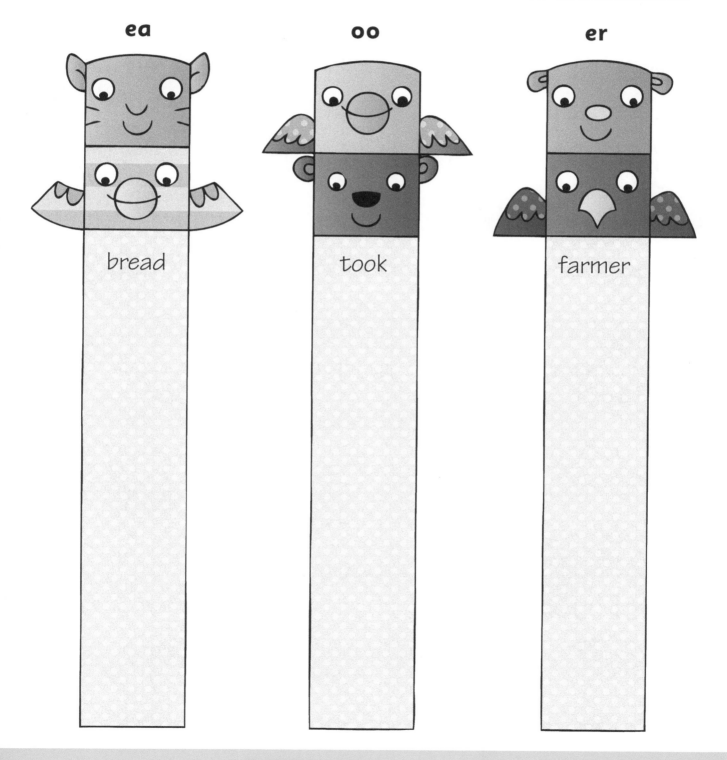

ea

bread

oo

took

er

farmer

How did you do?

51

Same sounds

Underline the sound that is the same in each of these word pairs. Write the letters that make this sound on the lines.

c<u>oi</u>n __oi__ = t<u>oy</u> __oy__

coil ____ = boy ____

bird ____ = burn ____

more ____ = fork ____

saw ____ = August ____

town ____ = cloud ____

bear ____ = hair ____

How did you do?

Two-syllable shopping

Say these words aloud and clap the syllable beats.
Put a mark between each beat.

Example: j a c k/e t

s u g a r

l e m o n

p a s t a

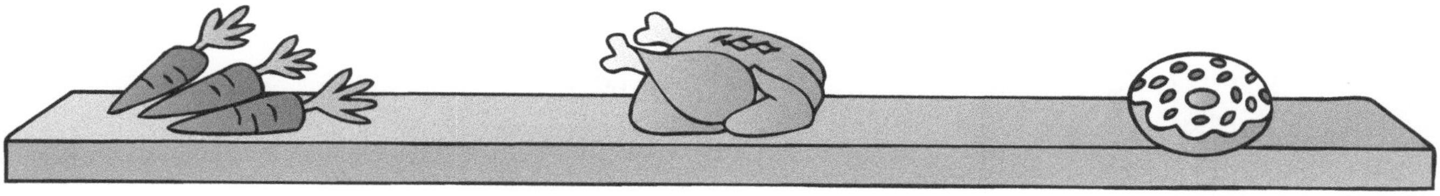

c a r r o t s

c h i c k e n

d o u g h n u t

Sound talk each syllable for the words on the list.
Cover each word and spell them out.

Shopping list

ruler

crayons

pencil

paper

comic

rubber

My spellings

How did you do?

Match the syllables

Clap the syllables as you say the word.

Say the words below. Draw a line to split them into two syllables. One has been done for you.

in/sect   sister   picture   puppet

ballet   trainer   pancake

Join the correct syllables to make six two-syllable words. Write them on the lines.

      _____

      _____

      _____

      _____

      _____

How did you do?

One or two syllables?

Say the words below aloud.
Clap the beats in each word.
If the word has more than one syllable,
draw a line between the beats.

You could turn this into a game by taking turns with a friend to pick a word and count the syllables.

w o r m	f l o w e r	t r e e
h e d g e h o g	w a t e r	w i n d o w
l a d y b i r d	f r o g	t a d p o l e
g r a s s	p i c n i c	s a n d w i c h

Write more words for minibeasts in the box below.
Draw lines to separate out the syllables.

How did you do?

55

Compound word sums

> Some words can be put together to make a new word. These are called compound words. For example: *class + room = classroom*

Complete these word sums. Your answer should be a compound word that describes the picture.

wind + _____

= _____

sun + _____

= _____

Write the compound words next to the correct description.

> bedroom   hairbrush   doorbell   beanbag   footpath

1. A path to walk on.   _____

2. A bag filled with beans.   _____

3. A bell for a door.   _____

4. A room with a bed.   _____

5. A brush for your hair.   _____

How did you do?

Two for one

Check your answers by making a list of the compound words you have made on a separate piece of paper. Do they look right?

Draw lines between words that can be joined together to make new words. The first one has been done for you.

sand

wind

bean

hand

lunch

tree

drift

star

wood

pit

stand

mill

box

light

stalk

top

How did you do?

Jigsaw pieces

Two words can be put together to make a compound word.
For example: *hand + bag = handbag*

Draw a line to split these compound words into two smaller words. Write the small words in the jigsaw pieces.

w a t e r / f a l l   t u g b o a t
s e a g u l l   k e y h o l e

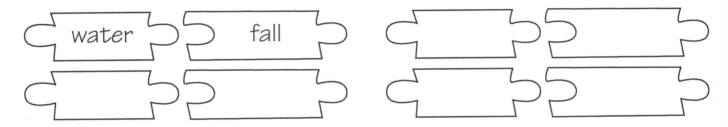

water   fall

Now make as many compound words as you can using the words below. Write them in the box.

room   eye   fly   butter   hand   fingers   lash
stand   bag   foot   ball   lid   bed   bath

How did you do?

Making opposites with un

We can add **un** to the beginning of words to show their opposites.

Add the correct labels to these pictures.

wrap	unwrap	happy	unhappy	tidy	untidy

tie   untie   zip   unzip   friendly   unfriendly

_____   _____

_____   _____

_____   _____

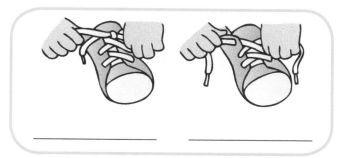

_____   _____

_____   _____

_____   _____

Use two of the words to complete this sentence.

I _____ up my coat when I go outside and

_____ it when I come back in.

How did you do?

59

Using un

Add **un** to the words below to make opposites.
Draw pictures to go with them.

happy   ⟶   _____happy

bend   ⟶   _____bend

Make these words beginning with **un**. Then use one of the new words to complete the sentence below.

un + kind = _____ | un + safe = _____

It is _____ to swim in a river full of crocodiles.

Use **un** to make the opposites of these doing words. Then use one of the new words to complete the sentence below.

un + wrap = _____ | un + fold = _____

I can't wait to _____ my birthday present.

How did you do?

Making un words

Do the word sums to make these **un** words.

1. un + lucky = _____

4. un + screw = _____

2. un + wind = _____

5. un + fit = _____

3. un + tie = _____

6. un + sure = _____

Use one of the **un** words above to match each picture.

_____   _____   _____

Use some of the words you have made to finish these sentences.

Try making up some of your own sentences using **un** words.

George was _____ about how to answer the question.

The team that lost the game were _____.

Myla could not _____ the cap.

How did you do?

s or es?

Add **s** or **es** to complete these words.

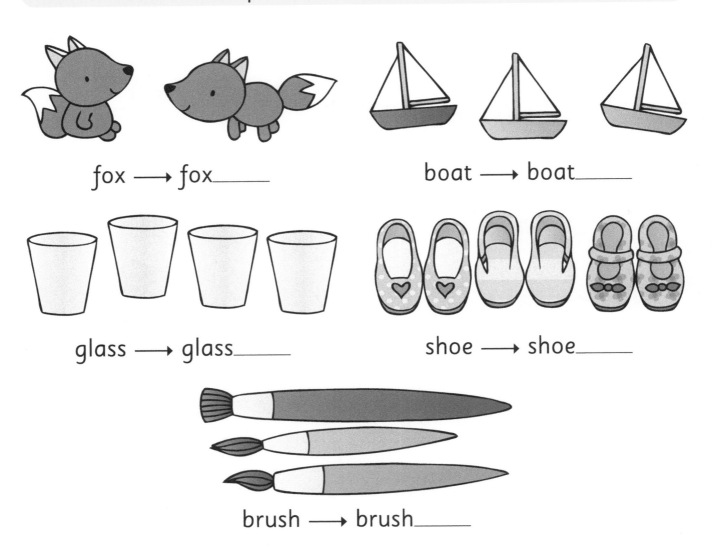

fox ⟶ fox_____

boat ⟶ boat_____

glass ⟶ glass_____

shoe ⟶ shoe_____

brush ⟶ brush_____

Write the missing words using **s** or **es**.

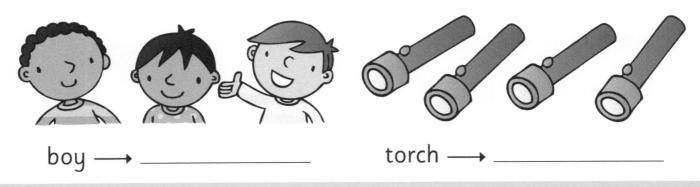

boy ⟶ _____

torch ⟶ _____

How did you do?

A school trip list

Alice has made a packing list for a school trip.
Add **s** or **es** to the ends of the words.

Two coat_____   Four dress_____

Two hat_____   Five short_____

Two brush_____

Three torch_____

Three sock_____

Add **s** or **es** to Alice's recount of the trip.

On Monday, two class_____ went on a camping
trip. Two big coach_____ came to pick us up.
At the campsite, we put up our tent_____. Then
we sat down to eat cheese sandwich_____ and
crunchy apple_____. Two bird___ flew down and
pecked the cake crumb_____.

How did you do?

My family

Depending on the person doing the action, you might need to add **s** or **es** to a verb. For example: *I throw the ball, but she throws the ball. I catch the ball, but he catches the ball.*

Add **s** or **es** to the words. Say the words to help you.

Dad read___ books.

Mum sing___ songs.

Gran wash___ the car.

Grandad fix___ robots.

Ted whizz___ round the park.

Ava build___ towers.

Add **s** or **es** to these words.

watch_____   clean_____

call_____   guess_____

Use some of the **s** and **es** words on this page to make up your own sentences. Write them on a separate piece of paper.

How did you do?

s or es sentences

Add **s** or **es** to these words. Say the words to help you.

> Words ending with a /**s**/ or /**z**/ sound are spelled with **s**. Words ending with an extra beat are spelled with **es**.

catch____   go____   push____   run____

Add **s** or **es** to these silly sentences.

Jack run____ up the mountain.

Maya catch____ a dinosaur.

Toby wash____ a giant's hands.

Sal cook____ a feast.

George jump____ over a river.

Meena watch____ dragons in the sky.

Add **s** or **es** to these words and then use the words to write your own silly sentence.

climb ⟶ climb____   brush ⟶ brush____

How did you do?

ing words

Add **ing** to the words below.

pull_____	play_____	kick_____
push_____	swing_____	march_____
climb_____	jump_____	catch_____

Use the words above to complete these sentences.

1. The boys are _____ the rope.

2. Dan and Tim are _____ their new go-cart.

3. Layla is _____ over Kelvin.

4. Maria is _____ up the rope ladder.

Use another of the **ing** words to make your own sentence.

_____

_____

How did you do?

Words with ed

Add **ed** to the end of these words.

jump_ed___	lift_____	dress_____
cook_____	snow_____	shout_____
rain_____	twirl_____	lick_____
laugh_____	plant_____	need_____

Choose one of the new words to match each picture. Write it in the space below.

_____   _____   _____

Use some of the words above to complete these sentences.

1. The path was wet because it had _____.

2. Lulu _____ her orange ice lolly.

3. The crowd _____ at the funny clown.

How did you do?

Adding ed

Sort the words in bold into their correct /**ed**/ sounds.
Write them in the correct boxes.

Read the words in bold aloud.
Listen to the sound that **ed** makes at the end of each word.

The farmyard was quiet and still, but then...

the owl **hooted**

the fox **howled**

the ducks **quacked**

the dog **barked**

the pigs **oinked**

the sheep **bleated**

the turkey **gobbled**

the bees **buzzed**

the farmer **yawned**

the tractor **spluttered**

and the day had begun.

Sounds like t	Sounds like id	Sounds like d

How did you do?

Making er words

Make these **er** words.

We can make nouns by adding **er** to verbs.

climb + er =

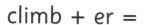

teach + er =

_____

row + er =

_____

Now make these words.

paint + er = _____

build + er = _____

walk + er = _____

sing + er = _____

Add **er** to these words to completel the labels.

jump_____

knock_____

buzz_____

mow_____

cook_____

How did you do?

Making new words

Add the three endings to each of the words in the balloons. Write the new words in the correct box below.

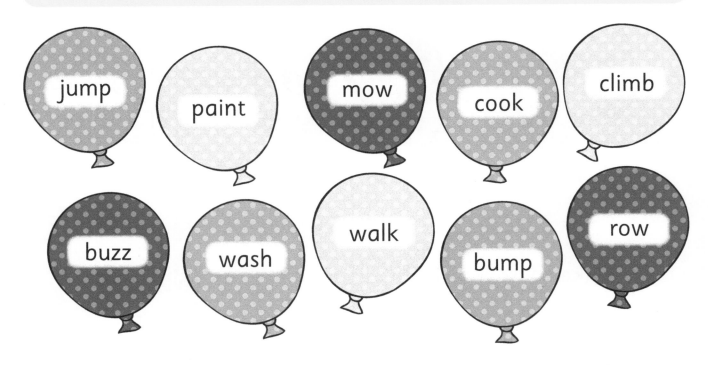

Add ing	Add ed	Add er
jumping	jumped	jumper

How did you do?

Small or smaller?

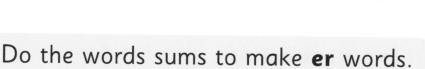

Do the words sums to make **er** words.

We can add **er** to a describing word to show it is less or more.

warm + er = _____

sharp + er = _____

cold + er = _____

hard + er = _____

Add **er** to make new words below.
Match the words to their opposites.

long____

fast____

high____

quiet____

small____

short____

slow____

low____

loud____

tall____

Use the **er** words to finish the sentences below.

1. My house is tall but my nan's house is _____.

2. My sister is loud, but I am _____.

3. A worm is slow but a tortoise is _____.

How did you do?

The greatest class

Do the word sums to make **est** words.

fast + est = _____

tall + est = _____

loud + est = _____

great + est = _____

Finish these sentences using the words you have made.

1. Dylan is the _____ runner in the class.

2. Sita is the _____ person in the class.

3. Pip is the _____ person in the class.

4. We are the _____ class in the school!

How did you do?

er or est?

Do the word sums to make **er** words and **est** words.

old

old + er =

_____

old + est =

_____

tall

tall + er =

_____

tall + est =

_____

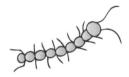

long

long + er =

_____

long + est =

_____

Use some of the words to complete the sentences.

1. The horse is _____ than the dog.

2. The cave is the _____ home.

3. The worm is _____ than the centipede.

How did you do?

My busy week

Add in the days of the week under each picture.

Monday

T_____

W_____

T_____

F_____   S_____   S_____

Complete the sentences adding the correct days of the week.

1. On _____ I went swimming.

2. On _____ I rode my bike.

3. On _____ I visited the zoo.

How did you do?

Tricky words space adventure

Draw a circle around the tricky words.

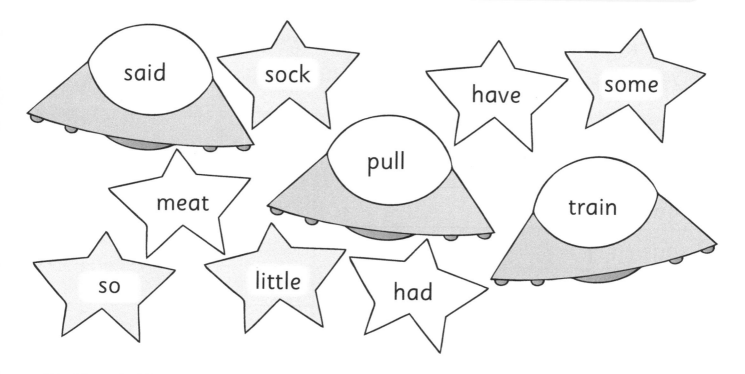

said sock have some pull meat train so little had

Read the tricky words. Put dots under the letters that you can sound out. Then underline the tricky parts.

ball   was   the

ask   friend   my

How did you do?

Read, cover, say, write, check

Read the first tricky word.
Cover the box, say the word and write it in the 'First try' box.
Check your answer. Then write the word again in the 'Second try' box. Do this for all the words.

Tricky words	First try	Second try
the		
says		
were		
they		
come		
small		
once		
school		
your		
push		

Add three more tricky words to the list.

How did you do?

Find the tricky words

Some words have tricky parts that are hard to sound out.
We have to know what they are and how to spell them.

Tricky words

the	a	do	to	today	of	said
says	are	were	was	is	his	has
you	your	they	be	he	me	she
we	no	go	so	by	my	here
there	where	I	come	some	one	once
ask	Mr	Mrs	when	little	class	friend
school	put	push	pull	full	house	our

Underline tricky words in the sentences below. Write two
more tricky-word sentences in the empty speech bubbles.

I can see my
best friend.

We need to
get to school.

Mrs Brown is
our class teacher.

Can Lee come to
my house for tea?

Mum said I could
have a little pet.

_____

_____

_____

_____

_____

_____

How did you do?

77

Postcard sentences

sharks   fish   starfish   jellyfish   octopus   crabs

clownfish   prawns   eel   stingray   seahorse

Ella is writing a postcard about her visit to an aquarium.
Use the words in the box above to finish the message.

Dear Jordan,

I am visiting my gran. Today,

we went to the fish aquarium.

In the large fish tank, I saw

_____

_____

_____.

Love,

Ella

Jordan Gaskin

1 High Street

Old Town

Devon

ZX1 3TD

How did you do?

The gingerbread man

Look at the pictures for the story. Write a caption for each picture.

1.

_____
_____
_____

2.

_____
_____
_____

3.

_____
_____
_____

4.

_____
_____
_____

5.

_____
_____
_____

6.

_____
_____
_____

How did you do?

Well done!

Cut-out your reward Ollie.

Name:

....

You have completed

Spelling and vocabulary

For ages 5–6

Age: ....

Date: ....